INTRODUCTION
TO ALGOL

Prentice-Hall
Series in Automatic Computation

George Forsythe, editor

BAUMANN, FELICIANO, BAUER, SAMELSON, *Introduction to Algol*
DESMONDE, *Computers and Their Uses*
DESMONDE, *Real-Time Data Processing Systems: Introductory Concepts*
SCHULTZ, *Digital Processing: A System of Orientation*
TRAUB, *Iterative Methods for the Solution of Equations*
VARGA, *Matrix Iterative Analysis*
WILKINSON, (Editor), *Rounding Errors in Algebraic Processes*

PRENTICE-HALL INTERNATIONAL, INC., *London*
PRENTICE-HALL OF AUSTRALIA, PTY., LTD., *Sydney*
PRENTICE-HALL OF CANADA, LTD., *Toronto*
PRENTICE-HALL OF INDIA PRIVATE LIMITED, *New Delhi*
PRENTICE-HALL OF JAPAN, INC., *Tokyo*

INTRODUCTION TO ALGOL

R. BAUMANN | *Mathematisches Institut der Technischen Hochschule München, Germany*

M. FELICIANO | *Mathematics Division Oak Ridge National Laboratory*

F. L. BAUER
K. SAMELSON | *Mathematisches Institut der Technischen Hochschule München, Germany*

PRENTICE-HALL, INC.
ENGLEWOOD CLIFFS, N.J.

Current printing (last digit):

13   12   11   10   9   8   7   6

Library of Congress Catalog Card No. 64-10740
Printed in the United States of America
47782 C

Revised and extended version of the ALGOL Manual of the ALCOR Group
Original Title: ALGOL Manual der ALCOR Gruppe
    Elektronische Rechenanlagen *3* (1961) No. 5, 206–212
           3 (1961) No. 6, 259–265
           4 (1962) No. 2, 71–86
   Oldenbourg, München, 1962

PREFACE

ALGOL has found interest throughout the computing community. The defining report[1] was not intended to be a primer, however, since its aim of strict syntactic and semantic description did not allow this. This book is intended to give a needed introduction to ALGOL, which should enable the nonspecialist, for whose benefit ALGOL was primarily conceived, to write clear and readable ALGOL programs from which a reasonable translator will produce efficient machine codes.

Emphasis is on the normal use of the language rather than on artificial examples exploiting tricky possibilities; ALGOL has these as does any other language. The treatment of constructions which appear to have limited practical importance has been minimized. The use of certain features which would either conceal the form of a program or lead to machine code of doubtful efficiency has been ignored. It may be said that this voluntary restriction still leaves an extremely powerful language, acceptable to anyone who wishes to use ALGOL as a tool and not just for ALGOL's sake. A potential user will not find it difficult to learn this "normal use" of ALGOL. For didactic reasons we have not always kept to the syntactical formalities of the ALGOL report. Punctuation marks required in the text have been suppressed wherever they could be wrongly interpreted as ALGOL symbols. It would be impossible to cover the scope of applications and difficulties by means of selected examples; however, a small set of exercises has been included in order to point out common programming mistakes and important features of the language. An attempt was made to have Parts I and II correspond to the forthcoming IFIP Subset ALGOL 60.

---

[1] J. Backus, et al. Report on the algorithmic language ALGOL 60, Num. Math. **2,** 106–36 (1960), Comm. Assoc. Comp. Mach. **3,** 299–314 (1960).

J. Backus, et al. Revised Report on the Algorithmic Language ALGOL 60, Num. Math. **4,** 420–53 (1963), Comm. Assoc. Comp. Mach. **6,** 1–17 (1963).

The ALCOR group,[2] a cooperative association primarily interested in the construction of ALGOL compilers and on common hardware representations, found it desirable to provide the users with a common manual thus promoting program exchangeability. The manual arose from courses and lectures and grew during practical experience using and compiling ALGOL. This book results from revisions and extensions of that effort. In preparing it the authors are greatly indebted to H. H. Bottenbruch, W. Gautschi, A. A. Grau, A. S. Householder, M. Paul, H. Rutishauser, H. R. Schwarz, J. Stoer, K. H. Wiehle, and Chr. Witzgall.

The defining report of full ALGOL 60 is included as an appendix. The corrections and amendments recommended in April 1962 in Rome, Italy are incorporated in this revised version, which is an officially approved IFIP (International Federation for Information Processing) document.

MUNICH

OAK RIDGE

---

[2] At present, members of the ALCOR group are:

Institut für Angewandte Mathematik der Eidenössischen Technischen Hochschule, Zürich

Rechenzentrum der Technischen Hochschule München

Institut für Angewandte Mathematik der Universität Mainz

Institut für Praktische Mathematik der Technischen Hochschule Darmstadt

Siemens & Halske AG, München

Institut für Angewandte Mathematik der Universität Bonn

IBM-Forschungsgruppe Wien

Oak Ridge National Laboratory, Oak Ridge, Tennessee

Telefunken GmbH, Backnang

Zuse KG., Bad Hersfeld

Dr. Neher Laboratory of the Netherlands Postal and Telecommunications Services, Leidschendam

Standard Electric Lorenz AG, Informatikwerk, Stuttgart

IBM–Deutschland, Sindelfingen

University of Illinois, Digital Computer Laboratory, Urbana, Ill.

Eurocomp G.m.b.H., Minden

Remington Rand G.m.b.H., Frankfurt/Main

Control Data G.m.b.H., Frankfurt/Main

Purdue University, Department of Computer Sciences, Lafayette, Indiana

University of Western Ontario, Department of Computer Sciences, London, Canada

University of Maryland, Computer Science Center, College Park, Maryland

Rechenzentrum der Christian Albrecht Universität Kiel

Kommission für Elektronisches Rechnen der Bayerischen Akademie der Wissenschaft, München

Mathematisches Institut der Technischen Hochschule München

University of Michigan, Computing Center, Ann Arbor, Michigan

CONTENTS

INTRODUCTION
TO ALGOL

INTRODUCTION

1. MODE OF OPERATION AND CAPABILITY OF DIGITAL COMPUTERS

The digital computer has astonishing capabilities as a tool for the experimental scientist. It is immediately evident that the use of such a tool requires thorough preparation. Accordingly, we shall first get briefly acquainted with the scope of this preparatory work, after which we shall investigate the methods of programming, that is, of setting up instructions for the machine.

The computer is no oracle. Without appropriate information it cannot answer the question how good will the weather be on the next weekend. With suitable preparation it is able to provide quantitative information which enables meteorologists to predict the weather on the basis of meteorological theories. The meteorologist bears the responsibility for it, and the prediction is as good as the theory which served as basis for the computation.

Put another way: the machine can do nothing that the user in principle could not also do; it can only do it faster. It gives no answers to vague questions and can work only on a precise set of instructions. Much work, however, is usually required to go from the original problem to be solved to this set of instructions. This work begins with the mathematization of the problem, that is, with the postulation of a mathematical model for the phenomenon under consideration.

Normally, this mathematical model consists of a number of conditions imposed on the variables which are used to describe essential parts of the phenomenon. In the case of the weather we have atmospheric pressure, temperature, humidity, wind velocity, etc. In general these conditions are not amenable to direct computational treatment. Methods must be found which permit calculation of values for the variables satisfying the conditions imposed on them. The development or selection of the method is the most important part of handling the problem. This must be done with great care since improper handling can yield completely misleading results.

Generally only approximations are computed because the exact solutions of the problem require numerically impractical passage to limits. Together with the development of the procedure one must then give an account of the goodness of the approximation. This usually clears the question whether the approximation corresponds to an acceptable modification of the originally conceived model.

An example of this is the use of difference methods to calculate the potential and current distribution in a conducting metal plate. This corresponds to the substitution of the plate by a grid of conducting wire. Sometimes the physicist can easily determine whether this model is useful, whereas it is very hard to establish strict mathematical limits to the error.

The preparation of the computational work starts once a method of solution has been selected. In simple cases this work is completely trivial. If, for instance, a formula given in a textbook or manual is to be evaluated, then it is best to undertake the evaluation directly. When an assistant is to do the work, he is given the book and the numbers needed for the computation. If the problem is more complicated, one must write down what should be done. The more there is to do, the more detailed the instructions, since less insight into the problem can be expected from the assistant.

The computing machine is merely an assistant which has no insight into what it is doing. Therefore, one must give it a set of instructions which clearly describes the process to the smallest detail. The machine executes these instructions word for word. In general it is not possible to predict what happens when one gives the machine an instruction that is not part of its limited repertoire. It may be that it stops working and points out that something is not in order. However, it may just as well continue working in a nonsensical manner. Accordingly, preparing the working procedure (the program) for a computing machine requires careful attention; in particular, a precise disposition and handling of all possible special cases.

2. PROGRAMMING

It is clear that we must write down the set of instructions that we want to give to the machine. However, we cannot use everyday language and expect the machine to receive instructions in the form of a letter or dictation. Instead we must adapt the language used to the capabilities of the machine.

Although the computing machine can be used in more general problems, in what follows we shall emphasize computation—more precisely, arithmetic computation. Arithmetic formulas which contain numbers, names denoting yet unknown quantities, and functions (such as *sin*, *cos*, and *ln*) have long been used to describe computational rules. Such formulas form a core embedded within a sequence of organizational statements which describe the flow of the computational process. Thus, for example, the execution of parts of the computation can be made to depend on certain conditions, or one can prescribe the number of times a part is to be repeated. Indeed, the power of the *automatic* computer comes from its ability to make precise decisions at definite places during the course of the computation in accordance with preassigned criteria.

Finally, the machine must receive specifications as to type and dimension of the initial data entering into the computation (input data) and the numerical values given as the result (output data). A complete set of instructions and rules written in such a manner that it uniquely defines the course of a computation from beginning to end, we will call a *program*.

The preparation of the program entails more than due consideration to the arithmetic and organizational capabilities of the machine. The simple-minded intelligence of the computer requires that the language used be formed according to stringent rules. The present manual explains the standardized formal language ALGOL (*algo*rithmic *l*anguage) which arose out of an international effort. ALGOL programs are largely independent of the properties of individual machines and are conveniently readable to a wide circle of interested people. To an ever increasing extent algorithms and programs are being written and published in ALGOL.

3. CODING

In addition to what has already been said the program must be written in such a way that the machine can receive it. The input data as well as the program must be reduced to the specific code for input medium of the particular machine. To do this one uses off-line equipment—for example, punching mechanisms, printers, and hand punches. The machine receives the code through input equipment such as paper tape and card readers.

4. INTRODUCTORY EXAMPLES

We consider two simple examples which show certain fundamental aspects of the use of automatic computers.

EXAMPLE 1

Let us consider the system of linear equations in two unknowns

$$2x + 3y = 5$$
$$3x + 5y = 4.$$

Using Cramer's rule we obtain the following solution:

(1) $$x = \frac{5 \cdot 5 - 4 \cdot 3}{5 \cdot 2 - 3 \cdot 3} \qquad y = \frac{2 \cdot 4 - 3 \cdot 5}{5 \cdot 2 - 3 \cdot 3}$$

We shall, therefore, give instructions to the machine to compute the expressions on the right side of (1) and to assign these numerical values to the variables x and y. In order to simplify the code we use the slanted slash for the division sign. For the purpose of clarity we introduce the symbol "$\times$" for the multiplication sign; it must be used for each multiplication. Using these conventions we now write

$$x = (5 \times 5 - 4 \times 3)/(5 \times 2 - 3 \times 3);$$
$$y = (2 \times 4 - 3 \times 5)/(5 \times 2 - 3 \times 3);$$

This program yields the right solution, but at the expense of superfluous computation. We should not forget that the machine follows each instruction to the letter and for this reason computes the expression

$$5 \times 2 - 3 \times 3$$

twice.

Therefore, we amend the program to read

$$d = 5 \times 2 - 3 \times 3;$$
$$x = (5 \times 5 - 4 \times 3)/d;$$
$$y = (2 \times 4 - 3 \times 5)/d;$$

This is a special program for obtaining the solution of a definite system of equations. We get a program valid for the general case only if we admit arbitrary coefficients,

$$a_1 x + b_1 y = c_1$$
$$a_2 x + b_2 y = c_2$$

The corresponding program will read

$$d = a1 \times b2 - a2 \times b1;$$
$$x = (c1 \times b2 - c2 \times b1)/d;$$
$$y = (a1 \times c2 - a2 \times c1)/d;$$

However, this program does not take all contingencies into consideration. We must provide for the case when d vanishes for the given values of $a1$, $a2$, $b1$, and $b2$.

$$d = a1 \times b2 - a2 \times b1;$$

if $d \neq 0$

then $\begin{cases} x = (c1 \times b2 - c2 \times b1)/d \\ y = (a1 \times c2 - a2 \times c1)/d \end{cases}$

otherwise continue the computation
in some special manner;

Here we encounter an essential part of the program that goes beyond mere computation, namely, a condition (if $d \neq 0$) on which the further course of

computation depends, and specifications as to what must be done (then ...
otherwise ...) on the basis of this condition. Notice also that the equality
sign in the condition has a meaning different from that in other parts of the
program.

EXAMPLE 2

In order to find the square root of a positive number a

$$x = \sqrt{a} \qquad a > 0$$

we can use Newton's method. This reduces to the following iteration

$$x_{n+1} = \frac{1}{2} \cdot \left(x_n + \frac{a}{x_n} \right) \qquad n = 1, 2, \ldots$$

Any positive number can be used as the initial value x_1.

The set of instructions is the same for each step of the iteration. It is
manifest that it need only be written once. The result of each step serves as
initial value for the next step. We can write the following program.

```
        y = x1;
2:      x = (y + a/y)/2;
        y = x;
```

        continue the computation at 2;

This program does not come to an end although it uses the iteration formula
correctly. We must tie into the "continue" statement some condition,
perhaps one that would interrupt the computation when two successive values
agree to 10 significant figures. Here we introduce the notation $abs(x)$ which
has the meaning of $|x|$.

```
        x = x1;
2:      y = x;
        x = (y + a/y)/2;
```

        if $abs(x - y) > (.5 \times 10^{-10}) \times abs(x)$

        then continue computation at 2
        otherwise end the computation;

We have already become acquainted with the conditional statement; here it
is connected with the continue statement which brings about the repetition of
a piece of program. Only in this way is it possible to describe completely the
flow of the computation without knowing the values of a and $x1$ on both of
which depend the number of required iterations.

I ALGORITHMIC LANGUAGE ALGOL ELEMENTARY PART

The algorithmic language ALGOL allows the machine user to avail himself of the familiar arithmetic conventions when formulating a program. The meaning of nonarithmetic symbols used in ALGOL is usually obvious.

Part I which is now to follow gives the basic symbols of ALGOL. It should make the reader familiar enough with the language so that he can write correct programs by himself.

This part is divided into six sections. The order of topics is chosen to enable the reader to recognize the systematic construction of the language, and also to write complete programs as early as possible.

1 BASIC SYMBOLS OF THE LANGUAGE

We shall first take a look at the basic symbols of the language and the ways and means by which they are put together to form other components. This type of construction is very much like that of a natural language in which words are constructed from letters.

1.1. THE BASIC SYMBOLS

1.1.1. LETTERS[1]

$$a \quad b \quad c \quad d \quad e \quad f \quad g \quad h \quad i$$
$$j \quad k \quad l \quad m \quad n \quad o \quad p \quad q \quad r$$
$$s \quad t \quad u \quad v \quad w \quad x \quad y \quad z$$
$$A \quad B \quad C \quad D \quad E \quad F \quad G \quad H \quad I$$
$$J \quad K \quad L \quad M \quad N \quad O \quad P \quad Q \quad R$$
$$S \quad T \quad U \quad V \quad W \quad X \quad Y \quad Z$$

1.1.2. DIGITS

$$0 \quad 1 \quad 2 \quad 3 \quad 4 \quad 5 \quad 6 \quad 7 \quad 8 \quad 9$$

1.1.3. OTHER SYMBOLS

$$+ \quad - \quad \times \quad / \quad \uparrow$$
$$. \quad {}_{10} \quad , \quad : \quad := \quad ;$$
$$(\quad) \quad [\quad]$$
$$= \quad > \quad < \quad \neq \quad \leq \quad \geq$$

---

[1] In the hardware representation used by the ALCOR group, lower case and upper case letters are not distinguished. This is analogous to the proposed SHARE hardware representation.

Spaces and new lines have no meaning in ALGOL since these are mere typographical features. However, they should be used liberally to improve the readability of the program.

1.2. NUMBERS

In this section we discuss the way in which numbers are constructed in ALGOL from the basic symbols. A number is represented in its most general form with a sign and a scale factor to the base 10 as in the conventional scientific notation.

EXAMPLE

$$+3.164981_{10}-4$$

Instead of this complete form, certain abbreviations are permissible; these omit unessential parts.

EXAMPLES

77	-317.092	$-126_{10}+04$
-551	$.5384$	$+04.719_{10}2$
$-_{10}30$	$+0.710$	$9.123_{10}+1$
$_{10}-7$	0	$2_{10}-6$
$+_{10}-3$		

1.3. IDENTIFIERS

A letter followed by a sequence of letters and digits constitutes an *identifier*.

EXAMPLES

$$A12 \quad ZET \quad M1A7 \quad x$$

A sequence of characters which contains letters and begins with a digit is inadmissible as an identifier. There is no restriction regarding the number of characters in an identifier.[1] Identifiers can be chosen freely and have no inherent meaning. However, the following sequences of letters may not be used as identifiers since they are reserved for special use.

abs	*arctan*	*cos*	*entier*
exp	*ln*	*sin*	*sign*
sqrt			

1.3.1. INPUT AND OUTPUT PROCEDURES

Input and output operations are not explicitly mentioned as part of ALGOL. However, there is a natural way in which they can be incorporated into the language. Since there is a need to communicate with the machine, we must use at least input and output operations which have been reduced to the

---

[1] Many compilers, however, differentiate identifiers up to only six leading characters.

barest essentials. Thus, let us agree that throughout this manual the identifiers

read   print

are reserved to have specific meaning, assuming that some handwritten routines have been added to the ALGOL compiler which implement this meaning.[1]

For the sake of simplicity, it can be understood that the input data (which are not an integral part of the program) nevertheless can only take any of the forms described in Section 1.2. As a rule the values of the result are given with as many decimal places as permitted by hardware limitations.

1.4. NONARITHMETIC SYMBOLS

The set of "other symbols" (cf. Section 1.1.3) was restricted with a mind toward coding and readability. We shall complete it by introducing symbols that look like words borrowed from common English.

The following symbols[2] appear in Part I (the elementary part of ALGOL).

array	**begin**	**comment**	**do**	**else**
end	**for**	**go to**	**if**	**integer**
real	**step**	**then**	**until**	**while**

These symbols are not to be regarded as words, that is, as sequences of letters. The fact that they appear in bold type emphasizes this circumstance. On this account the identifier "*end*" does not have the meaning of the nonarithmetic symbol "**end**".

---

[1] In the ALCOR group, these (and some more, which are discussed later) have been standardized by mutual agreement.

[2] In typewritten copy these symbols are underlined. In the hardware representation used by the ALCOR group, these symbols are represented by the English words in normal letters, enclosed by the escape symbol ', e.g., 'array' 'begin'.

2 ARITHMETIC EXPRESSIONS

The usual arithmetic formulas are constructed from numerical constants and symbols for variables. A formula gives a computational instruction which can be executed when each of the variables appearing in the formula has been assigned a numerical value. In this section we investigate the structure of expressions occurring in arithmetic formulas beginning with the simplest form, numerical expressions. This form is progressively extended by adding new components.

2.1. NUMERICAL EXPRESSIONS

The components of a simple numerical expression are unsigned numbers, (round) parentheses, and the operators[1]

$$+ \quad - \quad \times \quad / \quad \uparrow$$

Parentheses have the conventional meaning of arithmetic. In addition, we agree that the denominator of a fraction is always enclosed in parentheses unless it consists of a single nonnegative number. Naturally the denominator should not be the number zero.

EXAMPLES

$$3.1459$$
$$-1.2$$
$$(3.47_{10}-4 + 9.01_{10}+1)/4$$
$$9 \times 8 \times 7/(1 \times 2 \times 3)$$
$$(9 + 2.7)/(-3)$$
$$(((1.5 \times 3 - 4) \times 3 + 0.19_{10}1) \times 3 - 2.6_{10}3) \times 3$$
$$10 + 1.4/(1 + 0.9/(7 - 0.4/3))$$

---

[1] In full ALGOL 60 the operator symbol "$\div$" is also included. See footnote in Section 2.4.

The symbol "$\uparrow$" denotes exponentiation. For instance, $3.5 \uparrow 2.1$ has the meaning of $3.5^{2.1}$. The unsigned number or expression in parentheses to the left of the symbol "$\uparrow$" is the base; the one to the right is the exponent.

EXAMPLES

ALGOL form	Conventional form
$4.1 - 3 \uparrow 2$	$4.1 - 3^2$
$(4.1 - 3) \uparrow 2$	$(4.1 - 3)^2$
$3.2 \uparrow 2 + 5.2$	$3.2^2 + 5.2$
$3.2 \uparrow (2 + 5.2)$	$3.2^{2+5.2}$
$-4 \uparrow 2$	-4^2
$(-4) \uparrow 2$	$(-4)^2$
$4 \times 5/2 \uparrow 3$	$\dfrac{4 \cdot 5}{2^3}$
$5 \uparrow 2 \times 3$	$5^2 \cdot 3$

Also notice

$2 \uparrow 3 \uparrow 4$	$(2^3)^4$
$2 \uparrow (3 \uparrow 4)$	2^{3^4}

More about the evaluation appears in Section 2.3.

2.2. SIMPLE VARIABLES

Identifiers are used to designate variables. The variables can be *simple* or *subscripted*. The identifier of a subscripted variable is immediately followed by a list of subscripts enclosed in (square) brackets. Below we discuss simple variables only.

A simple variable can be used in an expression only if the following two conditions are met.

First: The top or heading of the program contains a declaration specifying the type of the variable: "integer" or "real".

Second: The expression is preceded by an assignment of a numerical value to the variable (cf. Section 2.2.2).

In the case of subscripted variables one needs a different declaration (cf. Section 4.2.1).

2.2.1. TYPE DECLARATIONS

The type declaration must be found at the beginning of the program. All variables appearing in the program must be declared. The declaration consists of a list of the variable identifiers following the symbols **integer** or **real**.

EXAMPLES

$$\textbf{integer} \quad n, \ M, \ i, \ Grad;$$
$$\textbf{real} \quad\quad a, \ ZET, \ I, \ lambda, \ B5;$$

The individual identifiers are separated from each other by means of the comma separator ",". The symbol ";" follows the last identifier to separate the declaration from the following one.

Note that type **real,** in accordance with standard mathematical use, includes type **integer**. The numerical value associated with the variable identifier may be given as input data or it may occur as an intermediate result in the program.

2.2.2. ASSIGNMENT OF NUMERICAL VALUES THROUGH INPUT

If the numerical value associated with an identifier is to be provided by input, then it is assumed that this value is waiting at the input equipment of the computing machine. This value needs only to be called in by the input procedure which has the form

$$read(\vee);$$

where $\vee$ stands for the variable identifier.

This statement reads into the machine the next number appearing in the parameter tape (or card). It then associates this value to the variable whose name is specified.

Several consecutive input statements can be included in a single one. The corresponding list of variables, each of which is separated from the others by a comma, replaces the single variable.

FORM $\quad\quad\quad\quad\quad\quad read(\vee, \ldots, \vee);$

The set of parameters in the input must occur in the order in which they are actually called in the run of the program.

EXAMPLES

$$read(A2);$$

In this case the parameter tape (or cards) must contain one number, say $1.279_{10} - 7$.

$$read(B10, \ B11, \ B12, \ B15);$$

The parameter tape (or cards) must contain four numbers, say

$$3.4_{10} - 1, \ 7.149, \ 825_{10}1, \ 9,$$

2.3. ASSIGNMENT OF NUMERICAL VALUES THROUGH EXPRESSIONS

If, on the other hand, the numerical value of a variable is calculated during the course of the program, then the assignment takes place through the assignment symbol ": =". The variable identifier is to the left and the expression is to the right of the assignment symbol.

FORM $\quad\quad\quad\quad\quad\quad \vee := \mathsf{E};$

Here E is a generic character for arithmetic expressions.

We are already acquainted with the simplest form of expressions, namely those built up from numbers. If a numerical value has been assigned to a definite variable, then the identifier of this variable can be used in expressions. Moreover, such expressions are constructed using the conventional arithmetic rules. Exception: no $\times$ may be dropped ($a \times b$, not $a\, b$).

Exponentiation is defined in general by

$$a^b = exp(b \times ln(a)) \qquad \text{if } a > 0.$$

However, if b is a positive integer, it is correspondingly defined by repeated multiplication of a (even if $a \leq 0$).

EXAMPLES

$$a4 := 3 \times a1 - 4 \times a2 + 5 \times a3;$$
$$AREA := R \uparrow 2 \times 3.14159265;$$
$$Q := (1 + 0.01 \times P);$$

2.3.1. EVALUATION OF EXPRESSIONS

Whatever arithmetic operations are found in an expression, numerical evaluation will follow the mathematical definitions as closely as possible. But it should be mentioned that the computer capability is limited; for example, rounding errors will be involved. Consequently two expressions which are mathematically equivalent may give slightly different results. This applies even to a single operation if there are alternative ways of computation, particularly in the case of exponentiation. Moreover, an expression may produce a whole number in the strict sense without this fact being recognized by the computer; in such a case the type real should be expected for the result.

If a definite evaluation is intended it may be necessary that it be specifically described. An example of this is the use of parentheses to specify the association of operations. Considerations of numerical analysis often force a careful formulation. For example, the explicit evaluation of high powers in polynomials is undesirable and can be avoided; see the example in Section 3.5.

2.3.2. TYPE OF THE VARIABLE TO WHICH A VALUE IS ASSIGNED

It stands to reason that the left-hand variable V should be declared to be of type integer only if the right-hand expression is integer-valued at least in the strict mathematical sense. In cases like $n \times (n + 1) \times (2 \times n + 1)/6$ evaluation of the expression E may lead to rounding errors, which, however, will be taken care of by proper round off if the variable to which the value is assigned is of declared type integer.

2.3.3. SPECIAL MEANING OF THE ASSIGNMENT SYMBOL

In this paragraph we point out explicitly the way in which assignment differs from equality. The very form of the assignment symbol emphasizes that there is a difference. The defining expression on the right of an assignment symbol and the variable identifier on the left are independent of each other. One can change the numerical value of a variable at any time by means of a new assignment. On this account, a variable identifier may appear on both sides of the assignment symbol. The expression on the right is evaluated with the "old value" of the variable. The resulting numerical value of the expression is then assigned as the "new value" of the variable.

EXAMPLE

$$i := i + 1;$$

The following examples serve to illustrate this circumstance.

(1) Computation of the sum

$$s = \sum_{i=1}^{i=3} a_i$$

making repeated use of the assignment statement:

$$
\begin{array}{l}
s := 0; \\
s := s + a1; \\
s := s + a2; \\
s := s + a3;
\end{array}
$$

After the last assignment statement s has the value of the sum.

(2) Evaluation of the polynomial

$$
\begin{aligned}
p(x_1) &= a_3 x_1^3 + a_2 x_1^2 + a_1 x_1 + a_0 \\
&= ((a_3 x_1 + a_2)x_1 + a_1)\, x_1 + a_0
\end{aligned}
$$

by means of repeated assignment statements:

$$
\begin{array}{l}
p := a3; \\
p := p \times x1 + a2; \\
p := p \times x1 + a1; \\
p := p \times x1 + a0;
\end{array}
$$

Following the last statement p has the value of $p(x_1)$.

2.3.4. MULTIPLE ASSIGNMENT

The assignment of the value of an expression can be extended to several variables. To do this it is necessary to alternate the variable identifiers with assignment symbols proceeding to the left of the first variable identifier.

FORM $$V := V := V := E;$$

The multiple assignment statement is possible only if all the variables occurring in the left part (that is, $V := V := V :=$) are of the same declared type. That is, if all have been declared **real** or all **integer**.

2.4. STANDARD FUNCTIONS

Full computational procedures for certain standard functions are built into the language. These functions can be summoned by means of definite identifiers. The argument for which the procedure is executed appears enclosed in parentheses immediately following the identifier. This argument consists of an arbitrary expression. In this form the standard functions can themselves be components of expressions. The standard functions are the following:

> $sqrt(E)$ the square root of E
> > (not defined for $E < 0$)
>
> $sin(E)$ the sine of E
> > (argument in radian measure)
>
> $cos(E)$ the cosine of E
> > (argument in radian measure)
>
> $arctan(E)$ the arctangent of E
> > $\left(\text{principal value between } -\frac{\pi}{2} \text{ and } +\frac{\pi}{2}\right)$
>
> $ln(E)$ the natural logarithm of E
> > (not defined for $E \leq 0$)
>
> $exp(E)$ the exponential function of E
> $abs(E)$ the absolute value of E

The values of these functions are of type real. The numerical value of the argument of *sqrt* or *ln* must lie within the domain of definition of the function. Otherwise, computation is discontinued and the machine may release a message explaining the difficulty.

The standard functions *sign* and *entier* have values of type integer. They are defined as follows:

> $sign(E)$ the sign of E
> > ($+1$ if $E > 0$, 0 if $E = 0$, -1 if $E < 0$)
>
> $entier(E)$ the largest integer not exceeding the
> > value of E

Observe that

$$
\begin{aligned}
entier\,(3.14) &= 3\\
entier\,(-7.5) &= -8\\
entier\,(2) &= 2\\
entier\,(-5) &= -5
\end{aligned}
$$

EXAMPLES

$$B + sign(B) \times sqrt(B \times B - 4 \times A \times C)$$
$$sqrt(A \times A \times A)$$
$$sin(alpha \times pi/180)$$

These functions enable us to specify (cf. Section 2.3.1) how the operation "$a \uparrow b$" is to be evaluated.[1] Thus we have that

$$y^{2.1} \text{ may be written as } exp(2.1 \times ln(y))$$

while

$$y^3 \text{ could be written as } y \times y \times y.$$

2.5. OUTPUT

The output procedure can be invoked as soon as all the variables occurring in an expression E have been assigned numerical values. The statement

$$print(E);$$

(which is the counterpart of the input instruction $read(V)$) instructs the machine to report the value of E by means of an output medium.

Several successive output statements can be combined into one.

FORM $print(E, \ldots, E);$

It stands to reason that the output is reported in a form which can be fed in again, that means in any suitable form described in Section 1.2.

---

[1] Integer division $a \div b$ for positive integers a, b is defined to be the integer indicating how many times b is contained in a. Therefore, the operation $a \div b$ may be written as

$$sign(a/b) \times entier(abs(a/b)),$$

which also defines it fully for any integers a and b, $b \neq 0$.

3 CONSTRUCTION OF THE PROGRAM

We are acquainted with the structure of the language through the assignment statements and type declarations, in a way, comparable to sentences in a natural language. In contrast to the type declaration which determines a property, the assignment statement commands an action. In general, we shall call *declarations* those forms in our language whose character is that of an agreement or definition. On the other hand, we denote by *statements* elements each of which has the character of a command or order.

3.1. SIMPLE STATEMENTS

We have already met the basic form of the simple statement in discussing the assignment of the numerical value of an expression (Section 2.2.2).

$$V := E;$$

To the computing machine it has the meaning of a direct request to compute the numerical value of E and associate this value to the variable V. As soon as this command is carried out completely the computing machine passes over to the next statement.

The same applies to the following statements:

read(V): assignment of a value through input equipment

print(E): release of the value of an expression through output equipment.

3.2. COMPOUND STATEMENTS

A sequence of simple statements uniquely prescribes a determined course of activity to the machine. Therefore, one can sometimes correctly consider this sequence as *one* statement. When writing down a program one expresses this fact by using the symbols

begin   end

A *compound statement* has the form

begin S; . . . S; S **end**

where S stands for an arbitrary statement,[1] even a compound statement and one of a kind to be introduced later.

The construction of a compound statement is necessary whenever a sequence of statements is to be treated as a unit, for instance, when the sequence is subject to a condition. Moreover, one can nest an arbitrary number of compound statements with the aid of no other symbols beyond those already mentioned. That is, the meaning of the symbol **begin** or **end** is uniquely determined by its position in the program. After all, the interpretation of the structure of **begin end** is exactly that of the parentheses structure in arithmetic expressions.

3.3. THE PROGRAM

There is a small step in going from the compound statement to a complete program. It consists in including all declarations necessary to the compound statement. It was previously mentioned that the type declarations must appear at the top of the program. This is true of all declarations.

Therefore, a program has the form

begin D; D; . . . D; S; S; . . . S; S **end**

where D stands for any declaration[2] and S for any statement.[2] The program is clearly divided into two parts; first, the declaration part and then the statement part. The declaration part is separated from the statement part by a semicolon. Thus, a program differs from a compound statement because of the declaration part.

3.4. COMMENTS

One can conveniently intersperse explanatory notes to make the overall plan of the program easier to understand. These explanations are introduced by the symbol **comment**. They are concluded with the symbol "; " which cannot appear inside of the text.

---

[1] S stands for a statement without the semicolon that separates it from the following one. Accordingly, the concluding semicolon of the last statement is missing. Nevertheless, it may be put in for the sake of clarity.

[2] Without the semicolon.

The complete construction

comment text;

may only follow ";" or "**begin**" and has no effect on the computational course of the resulting program.

Moreover, without using the symbol **comment**, explanatory notes can be written immediately after the symbol **end**. However, in this case the text will be concluded not only by the semicolon ";", but also by another **end**, or by the symbol **else**. This implies that here the text may not contain any of these three symbols.

3.5. EXAMPLE

At this point we want to write a simple example of a complete program which can be run in the machine.

The program computes the value of the polynomial of third degree

$$p(x) = a_0 + a_1 x + a_2 x^2 + a_3 x^3$$

for a specified argument x_1. The polynomial is given by means of its coefficients. In particular, let

$$a_0 = 1.5; \; a_1 = 116; \; a_2 = 27.4; \; a_3 = 0.987$$

and

$$x_1 = 134.68$$

The program:

```
begin comment Evaluation of a polynomial;
    real a0, a1, a2, a3, x1, p;
    read (a0, a1, a2, a3, x1);
    p := ((a3 × x1 + a2) × x1 + a1) × x1 + a0;
    print (p)
end
```

The following sequence of numbers must be in the input equipment

$$1.5, \; 116, \; 27.4, \; 0.987, \; 1.3468_{10}2,$$

4 LOOPS

Cyclic repetition of pieces of program is an important element of programming. The number of repetitions can sometimes be determined by means of a definite recursive scheme and other times it is established during the course of the computation. We discuss the first of these cases in the following section, the second case appears in Section 6.4.

4.1. REPETITION

We introduce a simple variable as the *controlled* or *loop variable* in order to characterize the iteration. The run of the variable is described *either* by stating the starting value, length of each step, and final value
in the form

$$\text{for } V := E \text{ step } E \text{ until } E$$

or

by the direct specification of a value in the form

$$\text{for } V := E$$

In each case E stands for an expression. The assignment symbol indicates that either form has the meaning of assigning a numerical value to the loop variable. After describing the behavior of the loop variable we set down the piece of program to be repeated, namely, a simple or compound statement; this forms a new statement.

FORM $\qquad\qquad \text{for } V := H \text{ do } S;$

where H stands for an abbreviation of either E **step** E **until** E or simply E (either of these forms is called a *for list element*).

Several for list elements can enter into a single loop statement.

FORM $\qquad\qquad \text{for } V := H_1, H_2, \ldots, H_n \text{ do } S;$

The sequence H_1, H_2, ..., H_n is called a *for list*. This form of the loop has the same effect as the compound statement

begin for $V := H_1$ **do** S; **for** $V := H_2$ **do** S; ...; **for** $V := H_n$ **do** S **end**;

EXAMPLE

We extend the problem used in the example of Section 3.5 in such a way that the polynomial is evaluated n times.

```
begin
      real a0, a1, a2, a3, z, p;
      integer n, i;
      read(a0, a1, a2, a3);
      read(n);
      for i := 1 step 1 until n do
          begin
              read(z);
              p := ((a3 × z + a2) × z + a1) × z + a0;
              print(p)
          end i
end
```

In order not to obscure the program the iterated statement should not alter the value of any quantity appearing in the expressions for starting value, length of step, and final value in the for list.

Loops can be nested one inside another. If we were to assume that in the preceding example the evaluations must be carried out for m polynomials, then the program can be extended as follows:

```
begin
      real a0, a1, a2, a3, z, p;
      integer m, n, i, j;
      read(m);
      for i := 1 step 1 until m do
          begin
              read(a0, a1, a2, a3);
              read(n);
              for j := 1 step 1 until n do
```

```
            begin
                read(z);
                p := ((a3 × z + a2) × z + a1) × z + a0;
                print(p)
            end j
        end i
end
```

The input equipment must have available the following list of values

$$m, a_0^1, a_1^1, a_2^1, a_3^1, n^1, z_1^1, \ldots, z_{n1}^1,$$
$$a_0^2, a_1^2, a_2^2, a_3^2, n^2, z_1^2, \ldots, z_{n2}^2, \ldots, z_{nm}^m$$

The superscripts refer to the polynomial to which the values belong.

4.2. SUBSCRIPTED VARIABLES

So far we have discussed cases in which the value of the controlled variable has no influence on the flow of the iterated statement. Even with the machinery at our disposal we cannot program so simple a process as

$$s = \sum_{i=1}^{i=n} x_i$$

in strict accord with the formula; that is, making use of the variable index. This necessarily leads us to admit indexed or subscripted quantities in the vocabulary of our language.

The name of a subscripted variable does not indicate a single numerical value but a field of values whose individual components are ordered. The subscript list, enclosed in brackets, is specified immediately following the identifier. This list consists of an expression for each subscript each of which is separated from the other by commas.

ALGOL form	Conventional form	Meaning
$x[1]$	x_1	First component of the vector x
$a1[i + 1, k]$	$a1_{i+1, k}$	The element in the $(i + 1)$-th row and k-th column of matrix $a1$
$Y[a[r + 1], l + 1]$	$Y_{a_{r+1}, l+1}$	The element in the a_{r+1}-th row and $(l + 1)$-th column of matrix Y.

In each of the last two cases, the intended component of the field is determined during the course of the computation when the expressions appearing in the subscript positions are evaluated. Our examples show that only integer valued subscripts make sense in ALGOL. Therefore rounding errors occurring in the evaluation of subscript expressions will be compensated by proper round off as in the case of expressions defining the value of variables of type integer (cf. Section 2.3).

Subscripted variables can be used as constituents of an expression only if a corresponding array declaration appears at the top of the program (cf. Section 3.3). A particular component of an array can then be used only after it has been assigned some value.

4.2.1. ARRAY DECLARATIONS

The required declaration establishes the number of subscripts and the bounds for each subscript position of a subscripted variable. The symbol for this declaration is **array**. For example,

$$\textbf{array } a[1:10, \, 1:20];$$

establishes that the identifier a is the name of a double subscripted variable which admits values between 1 and 10 in the first subscript position and between 1 and 20 in the second (the end values are included). The declaration is needed to reserve the space occupied by the array.

Several variables can be listed together when they are of the same type and have the same number of subscripts whose bounds agree individually. For example,

$$\textbf{array } A, \, B, \, C[1:5];$$

All the elements of an array are of the same type. Array declarations are understood to specify type **real** if no other type is declared. Should the declared type be **integer**, then the type and array declaration are included in one declaration **integer array**.

EXAMPLES

$$\textbf{array } A, \, B, \, C[1:10], \, D, \, EG[1:10, \, 1:20];$$
$$\textbf{integer array } N, \, M[1:4];$$

4.2.2. ASSIGNMENTS TO SUBSCRIPTED VARIABLES

The identifier of a subscripted variable is the collective name of a sequence of numerical values. Each admissible subscript combination determines a component of the variable. Everything that was said in Section 2 about simple variables is valid without reservations about the individual components of subscripted variables.

4.3. ITERATION

4.3.1. ITERATION WITH RESPECT TO SUBSCRIPTS

The loop variable may appear in a loop as a constituent of an expression in a subscript position. If so, then the iterated statement will be repeated with different components of the respective field or fields.

Therefore, the piece of program (cf. Section 2.3.1)

$$
\begin{aligned}
&S := 0;\\
&\textbf{for } i := 1 \textbf{ step } 1 \textbf{ until } 3 \textbf{ do}\\
&\quad S := S + a[i];
\end{aligned}
$$

has the meaning

$$
\begin{aligned}
&S := 0;\\
&S := S + a[1];\\
&S := S + a[2];\\
&S := S + a[3];
\end{aligned}
$$

4.3.2. GENERAL ITERATION

The controlled variable can also appear in expressions directly. Consider, for example, the following algorithm which computes

$$f(x, n) = x \cdot (x - 1) \cdot (x - 2) \cdot \ldots \cdot (x - n + 1).$$

$$
\begin{aligned}
&fact := 1;\\
&\textbf{for } i := 0 \textbf{ step } 1 \textbf{ until } n - 1 \textbf{ do}\\
&\quad fact := (x - i) \times fact;
\end{aligned}
$$

In the most general case of iteration the loop variable appears in the iterated statement directly in expressions and in subscript expressions (cf. example in Section 4.4.2).

4.4. EXAMPLES

4.4.1. EXAMPLE OF A LOOP STATEMENT WITH ITERATION OVER SUBSCRIPT

We consider simple operations on vectors. Let x and y be two vectors with n components. We determine the vector sum

$$s = x + y$$

the vector difference

$$d = x - y$$

and the projection of y on nonvanishing x

$$p = x \cdot \frac{(xy)}{(xx)},$$

where (xy) denotes the scalar product of x and y and (xx) the scalar product of x with itself.

```
begin
    real scalar, value, norm;
    integer i, n;
    array x, y, s, d, p[1:100];
    read(n);
    scalar := value := 0;
    for i := 1 step 1 until n do
        begin
            read(x[i], y[i]);
            s[i] := x[i] + y[i];
            d[i] := x[i] - y[i];
            print(s[i], d[i]);
            scalar := scalar + x[i] × y[i];
            value := value + x[i] × x[i]
        end;
    norm := scalar/value;
    for i := 1 step 1 until n do
        begin
            p[i] := x[i] × norm;
            print(p[i])
        end
end
```

The array declaration allows up to 100 components for x and y.

4.4.2. EXAMPLE OF A LOOP STATEMENT WITH GENERAL ITERATION

Let $a_0, a_1, \ldots, a_n$ be the coefficients defining a polynomial of the n-th degree

$$p(x) = \sum_{v=0}^{v=n} a_v x^v.$$

We evaluate its derivative

$$p'(x) = \sum_{v=1}^{v=n} v a_v x^{v-1}$$

at the point c using Horner's scheme. The problem resolves into the following program

```
begin comment Derivative of a polynomial;
      integer n, i;
      real p, c;
      array a[1:20];
      read(n, c);
      for i := 1 step 1 until n do
          read(a[i]);
      p := 0;
      for i := n step − 1 until 1 do
          p := p × c + i × a[i];
      print(p)
end
```

5 THE CONDITIONAL STATEMENT

Frequently the execution of a statement is tied to explicit conditions. For instance, the assignment of the value of an expression can be executed only if the expression is defined. Among other things, the arguments of the standard functions used in the expression must lie within their domain of definition, and the divisor must not be so small that the numerical value of the quotient lies outside the range of the machine. In particular, division by zero is not allowed.

Next we discuss conditional statements. With their help the execution of pieces of program can be made to depend on special conditions.

5.1. THE CONDITIONAL CLAUSE

In order to formulate conditions we avail ourselves of the comparison of the numerical values of arithmetic expressions. The ALGOL symbols used are

$$< \quad \leq \quad = \quad \geq \quad > \quad \neq$$

They have the obvious meaning. With these we can express relations of the form

$$E_1 \, \rho \, E_2$$

where ρ stands for one of the six symbols mentioned, and E_1 and E_2 for two arbitrary arithmetic expressions. The *conditional clause* consists of the symbol **if** followed by a relation.

FORM **if** $E_1 \, \rho \, E_2$

When such a clause comes up in the run of a program the numerical values of the expressions are calculated anew. It is then established whether the relation is true or false. The course of the program depends on this result.

5.2. THE OPTION

In the asymmetrical form of the conditional statement (the *option*) the conditional clause is followed by

then S;

where S is some statement,[1] simple or compound. Therefore, this conditional statement has the form

if B **then** S;

where B is an abbreviation of the relation $E_1 \rho E_2$.

S may not be a conditional statement, but notice the following permissible statement.

EXAMPLE

$$
\begin{aligned}
&\textbf{if } x > -1 \textbf{ then} \\
&\quad \textbf{begin} \\
&\qquad \textbf{if } x \neq 0 \textbf{ then} \\
&\qquad\quad x := 1/x \\
&\quad \textbf{end};
\end{aligned}
$$

If B is true, then S will be executed. If B is false, then S will not be executed. In this case the program continues immediately with the statement following S. One usually says that S was bypassed.

The asymmetry of the option is clearly depicted in the following diagram.

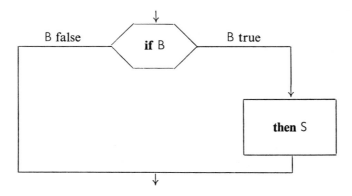

We borrow a simple example from Section 5 of the Introduction, namely the test of the determinant of a system of linear equations.

---

[1] Without the semicolon.

$$det := a1 \times b2 - a2 \times b1;$$
if $det \neq 0$ **then**
    begin
        $x := (c1 \times b2 - c2 \times b1)/det;$
        $y := (a1 \times c2 - a2 \times c1)/det$
    end;

Here the conditional statement causes the statements assigning values to x and y to be bypassed in case the determinant vanishes.

5.3. THE ALTERNATIVE

We make use of the *alternative* when we also want to provide a special set of instructions in case the condition is not fulfilled. We use the form[1]

if B **then** S_1 **else** S_2;

If B is true, then statement S_1 will be executed and S_2 bypassed. On the other hand, if B is false, then S_1 will be bypassed and S_2 executed. In both cases computation will continue with the statement next following the conditional statement.

The schematic representation points out clearly the symmetric structure of this form.

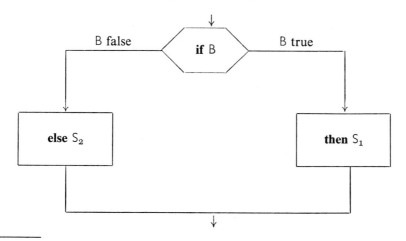

---

[1] S_1 and S_2 are statements without the semicolon. In particular, S_1 may not be followed by a semicolon.

In their turn, S_1 and S_2 can be simple or compound statements.   Moreover, if the statement next following **then**, that is, S_1 is a simple statement, it may not be a loop or conditional statement (however, cf. example in Section 5.2).

5.4. EXAMPLE

We consider a program to solve the quadratic equation
$$ax^2 + bx + c = 0$$
with arbitrary real coefficients a, b, c. This program serves as an example of the use of the alternative and of the nesting of conditional statements.

The program starts by calling in the coefficients a, b, c. It is formulated so that the organization of the output format allows us to recognize clearly the kind of solution. The only cases which are not distinguished from each other are the following:

$a \neq 0, b = c = 0$ (a vanishing double root)
$a = 0, b \neq 0, c = 0$ (a vanishing simple root)
$a = b = c = 0$ (undetermined solution).

```
begin comment: The solution of the quadratic equation
               a × x × x + b × x + c = 0 with arbitrary
               real coefficients a, b, c;
  real a, b, c, x1, x2, real part, imaginary part,
       contradiction, discr, r;
  read(a, b, c);
  x1 := x2 := real part := imaginary part := contradiction := 0;
  discr := b × b − 4 × a × c;
  if a ≠ 0 then
      begin
        if discr ≥ 0 then
          begin
            r := sqrt(discr);
            if b ≠ 0 then
                begin
                  x1 := −(b + sign(b) × r)/(2 × a);
                  x2 := c/(a × x1)
                end b
            else
                begin
                  x1 := +r/(2 × a);
                  x2 := −x1
                end
          end 2 real solutions
```

```
            else
                begin
                    r := sqrt(abs(discr));
                    real part := -b/(2 × a);
                    imaginary part := r/(2 × a)
                end 2 conjugate complex solutions
        end a not equal to 0
    else
        begin
            if b ≠ 0 then
                begin
                    x2 := -c/b
                end 1 real solution
            else
                begin
                    contradiction := c
                end solution undetermined
        end a equal to 0;
    print(x1, x2, real part, imaginary part, contradiction)
end
```

6 JUMPS

Loops and conditional statements cause a change in the dynamic course of the program as opposed to the sequence in which the statements were written down. To be sure, when these statements are used, the flow of the program is well mapped out. There are provisions to alter the normal flow of a program when neither of the above-mentioned schemes can be used; however, some restrictions must be observed.

6.1. LABELS

Every statement can be marked with a label. Identifiers[1] may be used as labels. The symbol ":" is used as a label separator. A labeled statement has the form

$$\mathsf{L} : \mathsf{S};$$

where L denotes a label and S a statement (simple or compound). We say that L is *attached to the statement* S. Labeled statements are considered as statements in the usual sense. They can be used without restrictions as constituents of compound statements.

EXAMPLES

$$1237: A := (R + R) \times 3.14;$$
$$B: x := y - a \times a;$$
$$determinant: D := a1 \times b2 - b1 \times a2;$$

Labels can be used to enhance the clearness of a program by using them as subtitles or numbering schemes. Moreover, the jump statement depends heavily on the use of labels.

---

[1] In full ALGOL 60 also unsigned whole numbers.

34

6.2. THE JUMP STATEMENT

Jumps can be constructed with the help of the symbol **go to**. The jump statement consists of this symbol followed by a label.

FORM   **go to** L;

6.2.1. JUMPS OUT OF LOOPS OR CONDITIONAL STATEMENTS

Frequently the jump statement is used to jump out of a loop or a conditional statement. In both cases the course of execution of the statement (either the loop or the conditional statement) is completely interrupted and not resumed later.

The loop variable retains its last assigned value when a loop is left prematurely. If the loop is terminated according to its regular course the value of the loop variable is thereafter no longer defined. When used together with a conditional statement the jump can be used to interrupt the sequence of a piece of program by means of a numerical condition. This case frequently appears in iteration processes (cf. Section 6.3).

6.2.2. INADMISSIBLE JUMPS

A jump from outside into a loop is inadmissible. More precisely, a jump to a labeled statement inside a loop must itself be made within the loop. If the jump into a loop is made from outside the loop, then the value of the loop variable is not defined.

On the other hand, a jump into a conditional statement is admissible. The flow of the program is well defined by the schematic representations in Sections 5.2 and 5.3.

6.3. EXAMPLE

We formulate a complete program that serves as an example of the use of the jump. The program determines the third root of a real number a by an iteration process. This iteration scheme is an application of Newton's method according to which

$$x_{n+1} = \frac{1}{3} \cdot \left(2x_n + \frac{a}{x_n^2} \right).$$

The initial value x_0 is specified and the iteration process continues until two successive approximations agree to 9 significant figures.

```
begin comment: Determination of the cube root;
       real a, approximation value, x, y;
       read(a, approximation value);
          x := approximation value;
```

Newton: $y := x$;
$\qquad\quad x := (2 \times y + a/(y \times y))/3$;
$\qquad\quad$ **if** $abs(y - x) > .5_{10}-9 \times abs(x)$ **then**
$\qquad\qquad$ **go to** *Newton*
$\qquad\quad$ **else** *print*(x)
end

6.4. ANOTHER FORM OF LOOP STATEMENT

The above example leads us to consider loops in which the number of times a statement is repeated is established during the course of the computation (cf. Section 4). The form of this loop statement is

$$\textbf{for } V := E \textbf{ while } B \textbf{ do } S;$$

where V, E, B, and S have the usual meaning. The form E **while** B is an additional for list element and may be used in a for list (cf. Section 4.1). Roughly, S will be repeated as long as condition B holds; more precisely, this loop may be interpreted as follows.

begin
$\quad$ L: V := E;
$\qquad$ **if** B **then**
$\qquad\quad$ **begin**
$\qquad\qquad$ S;
$\qquad\qquad$ **go to** L
$\qquad\quad$ **end**
end

The example in Section 6.3 can be rewritten as follows.

begin comment: Determination of the cube root;
$\qquad$ **real** a, *approximation value*, x, y, d;
$\qquad$ *read*$(a$, *approximation value*$)$;
$\qquad$ $x :=$ *approximation value*;
$\qquad$ $d := abs(x)$;
Newton: $y := x$;
$\qquad$ **if** $d > .5_{10}-9 \times abs(x)$ **then**

```
        begin
            x := (2 × y + a/(x × y))/3;
            d := abs(x − y);
            go to Newton
        end;
    print(x)
end
```

This program has the same effect as

```
begin comment: Determination of the cube root;
        real a, approximation value, x, y, d;
        read(a, approximation value);
        x := approximation value;
        d := abs(x);
        for y := x while d > .5₁₀−9 × abs(x) do
            begin
                x := (2 × y + a/(x × y))/3;
                d := abs(x − y)
            end;
        print(x)
end
```

II ALGORITHMIC LANGUAGE ALGOL — FURTHER CONSTRUCTIONS

In the second part which is now to follow the formal language ALGOL will be extended further. In it are introduced elements of the language which make possible elegant and convenient programming of complicated computational processes.

In Sections 7 through 9 are treated extensions to the language which can be associated with Sections 3 through 6 according to the following outline.

Elementary part	Further constructions
3	7
4	8
5	—
6	9

Section 10 deals with procedures, elements of the language which are related with the technique of subroutines occurring in the domain of internal machine coding.

7 BLOCK STRUCTURE

Up to now all programs have consisted of *one* declaration part and *one* statement part. We shall now get acquainted with the possibility of constructing a program composed of several units, each comprising a declaration part and a statement part. These units will be called blocks. The scope of validity of the declarations found in the individual block is accurately prescribed by means of the block structure of the program.

7.1. NESTING OF BLOCKS

In a program (cf. Section 3.3) any statement can be replaced by a construction of the form

$$\textbf{begin } D; D; \ldots; D; S; S; \ldots; S \textbf{ end}$$

This structure we will call a *block*. Therefore, the program is itself a block. A precise formulation of the concept of a *program* will be given later (cf. Section 7.3). Within the program blocks can be arbitrarily nested or put in a row.

We shall use the following conventions. A block is *subordinate* to a block containing it. A block is *dominant* with respect to any of its subordinate blocks. *Parallel* blocks are subordinate to the same hierarchy of blocks.

As in the case of compound statements (cf. Section 3.2) the block structure is clearly established by the position of the symbols **begin** and **end**. Each **begin** immediately followed by a declaration part introduces a new block; the corresponding **end** concludes it. A block can be labeled in its entirety just as can a simple or compound statement. In this connection the label is placed in front of the introducing symbol **begin**.

We illustrate some of these ideas by means of a schematic diagram.

41

```
                              ·   ·   ·
                                ·   ·   ·
   ┌─────── B1:   begin
   │                 D; D;...; D;
   │                 S; S;...; S;
   │    ┌───── B2:       begin
   │    │                    D; D;...; D;
   │    │                    S; S;...; S;
   │    │  ┌── B3:              begin
   │    │  │                        D; D;...; D;
   │    │  │                        S; S;...; S
   │    │  │                    end
   │    └──┘                end;
   │                     S; S;...; S;
   │    ┌───── B4:       begin
   │    │                    D; D;...; D;
   │    │                    S; S;...; S
   │    └─────            end
   └──────────       end;
                     S; S;...; S;
   ┌──────── B5:   begin
   │                 D; D;...; D;
   │                 S; S;...; S;
   │    ┌───── B6:       begin
   │    │                    D; D;...; D;
   │    │                    S; S;...; S
   │    └─────            end
   └──────────       end;
                              ·   ·   ·
                                ·   ·   ·
```

For the sake of simplicity a block is identified by the label attached to it. In connection with the above diagram, among others, the following statements are true:

> B1 is parallel to B5.
>
> B4 is parallel to B2 and to no other block.
>
> B3 is subordinate to B2 and B1.
>
> B2 is subordinate to B1 and dominant to B3.
>
> B1 is dominant to B2, B3, and B4.

7.2. SCOPE OF VALIDITY OF DECLARATIONS

In general, those elements of the language which require a declaration shall be called *quantities*. Within its scope of validity the declaration designates a name to denote a quantity and establishes definite properties of this quantity. The block structure determines the scope of validity of the declaration.

Simple and subscripted variables are examples of quantities. We further stipulate that the appearance of a label attached to a statement (cf. Section 6.1) is considered a declaration for the label which is valid for the innermost block containing the labeled statement. For the sake of simplicity we count labels among the quantities. We shall encounter yet further kinds of quantities.

The following rules are valid for declarations:

(1) Each name is used to denote one quantity of a block.[1]

(2) In general, a declared name should appear in the static sequence of the program (that is, in the order written down) only after its corresponding declaration is completed.[2]

(3) Any declaration appearing in the declaration part of a block is valid for the whole block; in particular, it is valid for all subordinate blocks.

(4) An individual declaration is temporarily suspended for a subordinate block if a new declaration referring to the same name appears in the declaration part of this block. As long as the new declaration is valid, the use of the name in the manner characterized by the earlier declaration is withheld.

(5) All declarations within a block are nullified on exit from that block. Declarations suspended for that block according to (4) take effect again.

The rules allow a manifold use of the same name in different blocks. However, for the sake of clarity, different declarations concerning the same name should be avoided in a program. Of course, there may be weighty reasons against this (for example, firmly adopted nomenclature).

From the fact that a jump statement can use only declared labels it follows immediately that a jump statement can lead only to a place in the same block or a dominant block. A jump statement outside of a block, which by circumventing the declaration part of the block leads to the interior of the block, is not defined; therefore it is inadmissible (cf. Section 6.2.2. for a similar circumstance).

7.3. SCOPE OF VALIDITY OF ASSIGNED VALUES

The quantities declared within a block are said to be *local* relative to the block. Furthermore, other quantities declared in dominant blocks can appear

---

[1] We shall get acquainted with an exception to this general rule in Section 10.1.2.

[2] With the exception of labels.

in a subordinate block; these quantities are said to be *nonlocal* or *global* relative to the subordinate block. Upon leaving a block all information about local quantities together with the declarations is lost. For example, variables lose their assigned values.

This means practically that storage space hitherto used to keep this information is freed and is at disposal for the next block. Because of this mode of operation, an economical use of storage space can be effected for parallel blocks (cf. Section 7.5 for an example). In nested blocks, if a declaration is temporarily suspended in accordance with Rule 4 of Section 7.2, then the value last assigned to the quantity in the dominant block is maintained. As long as the declaration is suspended the value of the quantity is withheld since corresponding to the attached name another declaration is valid. When the old declaration takes effect again, then the assigned value is again available. Thus, in the program

```
begin real a;
    a := 1;
        begin real a;
            a := 2;
            print(a)
        end;
    print(a)
end
```

two numbers, 2 and 1, are printed in that order.

In the light of the block structure, the concept of a "program" can be established definitively. A block which contains the declarations of all quantities appearing in itself is called a *program*.

It follows that a program cannot contain quantities which are global with respect to its outermost block. All value assignments of the local quantities take place within the program. Jumps leading out of the program are not possible.

7.4. DYNAMIC ARRAY DECLARATIONS

The block structure renders possible an extension to the form of the array declaration discussed in Section 4.2.1. The subscript bounds, hitherto given explicitly in the form of whole numbers, can now be given by means of appropriate arithmetic expressions, presumably integral valued, provided that these expressions contain no variables local to the block under consideration.

Obviously, the nonlocal variables must have been declared and corresponding value assignments must have taken place.

The following piece of program shows a typical use of the dynamic array declaration.

> **begin integer** n, m;
> $read(n, m)$;
>   **begin array** A $[1:n, 1:m]$;

7.5. EXAMPLE

We extend the problem of Section 4.4.1, given two vectors x and y, each having n components, to determine the projection p of x on the sum vector $s = x + y$,

$$p = s \cdot \frac{(sx)}{(ss)},$$

the projection q of x on the difference vector $d = x - y$,

$$q = d \cdot \frac{(dx)}{(dd)},$$

and the absolute value of the difference of the lengths of p and q,

$$|D| = \left| \frac{(sx)}{(ss)} \cdot \sqrt{(ss)} - \frac{(dx)}{(dd)} \cdot \sqrt{(dd)} \right|.$$

The program should be laid out in such a way that for arbitrarily chosen n only $3n$ storage locations are required for the arrays. It is further supposed that a punched tape (or cards) containing the components $\xi_1, \xi_2, \ldots, \xi_n$ of the vector x and $\eta_1, \eta_2, \ldots, \eta_n$ of the vector y in the given order exists already.

The problem can be solved by determining p and q in two parallel blocks.

> **begin integer** n;
> $read(n)$;
>   **begin integer** i;
>   **real** s $value$, d $value$, p $norm$, q $norm$, $scalar$;
>   **array** x, $y[1:n]$;
>   **for** $i := 1$ **step** 1 **until** n **do**
> $read(x[i])$;
>   **for** $i := 1$ **step** 1 **until** n **do**
> $read(y[i])$;
> s $value := d$ $value := 0$;
>   **begin array** $s[1:n]$;
> $scalar := 0$;
>   **for** $i := 1$ **step** 1 **until** n **do**

```
            begin
                s[i] := x [i] + y[i];
                scalar := scalar + s[i] × x[i];
                s value := s value + s[i] × s[i]
            end;
        p norm := scalar/s value;
        for i := 1 step 1 until n do
            print(s[i] × p norm)
    end;
    begin array d[1:n];
        scalar := 0;
        for i := 1 step 1 until n do
            begin
                d[i] := x[i] − y[i];
                scalar := scalar + d[i] × x[i];
                d value := d value + d[i] × d[i]
            end;
        q norm := scalar/d value;
        for i := 1 step 1 until n do
            print(d[i] × q norm)
    end;
    print(abs(p norm × sqrt(s value) − q norm × sqrt(d value)))
end
end
```

8 PROPOSITIONS AND CONDITIONS

Up to this point conditions have been formulated only by means of simple comparisons. Hence the combination of several conditions was always carried out by nesting conditional statements. Now we treat the possibility of combining several propositions in a single expression. This section introduces the truth values of such propositions, Boolean variables, and the assignment of values to these variables. The elements of the language required to represent the Boolean expressions are taken from the propositional or sentential calculus of mathematical logic.

8.1. LOGICAL OPERATIONS

A simple comparison of the kind introduced in Section 5.1,

$$E_1 \, \rho \, E_2$$

always represents one of the logical values "true" or "false" in much the same way that an arithmetic expression represents a numerical value. In contrast with arithmetic expressions, a linguistic construct which determines a logical value we call a *Boolean expression*, or better, a *proposition*. Thus, comparisons of the above-mentioned form are propositions. New propositions can be constructed with the help of the binary operations conjunction, disjunction, implication, and equivalence, and the unary operation negation. The symbols shown below, which are read as indicated in the line next following, serve as symbols for the corresponding operations

negation	conjunction	disjunction[1]	implication	equivalence
$\neg$	$\wedge$	$\vee$	$\supset$	$\equiv$
not	and	or	implies	is equivalent to

---

[1] This has the same meaning as that of the expression commonly used in legal documents, and/or.

EXAMPLES

$$(A > 5) \lor (B \geq 1)$$

Read A greater than 5, or B not less than 1.

$$(A \times B \geq C + D) \equiv (abs(Z1 + Z2) > m)$$

Read $A \times B$ not less than $C + D$ is equivalent to $abs(Z1 + Z2)$ greater than m.

The truth values of the unary and binary logical expressions are given in the following table (B_1 and B_2 stand for Boolean expressions).

B_1	true	true	false	false
B_2	true	false	true	false
$B_1 \land B_2$	true	false	false	false
$B_1 \lor B_2$	true	true	true	false
$B_1 \supset B_2$	true	false	true	true
$B_1 \equiv B_2$	true	false	false	true
$\neg B_1$	false	false	true	true

More complex propositions are possible by admitting B_1 and B_2 (in the above table) to be not only elementary but also arbitrary propositions. The precise evaluation of a proposition is obtained by the rule of precedence which clearly establishes a hierarchy of binary logical combinations for each compound proposition. Since arithmetic operations and relations can appear in a Boolean expression the rule is valid for any of the combinations listed (cf. Section 2, "Arithmetic Expressions", and Section 5.1 "The Conditional Clause"). It is understood that in a proposition, at least one of the operations of levels 6 to 9 (see table below) must appear between any two comparisons. The following hierarchical arrangement defines the rank of an operation with respect to a combination.

Level	Operation symbol	Operation
1	$\uparrow$	arithmetic operation
2	$\times$ / $\div$	arithmetic operation
3	$+$ $-$	arithmetic operation
4	$<$ $\leq$ $=$ $\geq$ $>$ $\neq$	relational operation
5	$\neg$	negation
6	$\wedge$	conjunction
7	$\vee$	disjunction
8	$\supset$	implication
9	$\equiv$	equivalence

In a particular construct the operations are executed in a sequence from the highest level (smallest number) to the lowest level (largest number). Operations of the same level are executed in order from left to right. As in the case of arithmetic expressions parentheses can be used to control the order of execution of the operations.

EXAMPLES

The form

$$0 \leq x \leq 1$$

is not admissible; however, one can write

$$0 \leq x \wedge x \leq 1$$

The arithmetic expression

$$a/b \times c$$

is taken to mean $(a/b) \cdot c$ because the operations $/$ and $\times$ have the same rank. If $a/(b \cdot c)$ is desired, then

$$a/(b \times c)$$

should be used.

The comparison

$$x < y + z$$

is executed as $x < (y + z)$ because $+$ has higher rank than $<$.

The propositions
$$x = 3 \lor 1 \le x \land x \le 2$$
and
$$(x = 3) \lor ((1 \le x) \land (x \le 2))$$
are executed in the same order. However,
$$(x = 3 \lor 1 \le x) \land (x \le 2)$$
is a different proposition. This follows from the fact that if x has the value 3 the original proposition has value "true" and the last proposition has the value "false."

8.2. BOOLEAN VARIABLES

The *logical values* (*truth values*)

true   false

can be interpreted without reservation as new kinds of values appearing side by side with the usual arithmetic values (numbers) represented by means of digits. Every proposition represents a value from this class of logical values just as every arithmetic expression represents a numerical value.

Therefore, it is natural to introduce a new variable besides those hitherto known of types **real** and **integer**. We call the new variables *Boolean variables* and use the symbol

Boolean

to designate the type. For arrays of Boolean variables the symbol combination **Boolean array** is used.

Everything that was said in Section 2.2 about variables and in Section 2.3 about expressions is valid respectively for Boolean variables and propositions if the following replacements are made. In Sections 2.2.1 and 2.2.2 replace **integer** or **real** by **Boolean** and numerical values by logical values **true** or **false**; in Section 2.3 replace arithmetic expression E by Boolean expression (or proposition) B. Also in Section 4.2 replace **array** or **integer array** by **Boolean array**.

Variables of type **Boolean** are elementary propositions and, as in the case of comparisons, can appear in compound propositions.

It follows that Boolean variables can be used freely in Boolean expressions provided that the variables involved have been previously declared and assigned values. The assignment of a logical value to a variable of type **real** or **integer** as well as the assignment of a numerical value to a variable of type **Boolean** is not admissible.

8.3. FORMULATION AND USE OF CONDITIONS

In the most general form of the conditional clause (cf. Section 5.1) an arbitrary Boolean expression B may replace the simple relation

$$E_1 \, \rho \, E_2$$

FORM   **if** B

The use of the conditional clause to formulate conditional statements is fully discussed in Sections 5.2 and 5.3. With their help the execution of statements can be made to depend on special conditions.

An arithmetic or a Boolean expression can also be made subject to a condition, but only in the form of the alternative (corresponding to Section 5.3).

The *conditional arithmetic expression* has the form

$$\textbf{if } B \textbf{ then } E_1 \textbf{ else } E_2$$

If B has the value **true**, then the value of this arithmetic expression is the value of E_1; otherwise, the arithmetic expression has the value of E_2. Of course, E_1 and E_2 are arithmetic expressions. Corresponding to the rule of construction of the alternative, E_1 may not be a conditional arithmetic expression unless it is enclosed in parentheses. It is, of course, admissible to enclose also E_2 in parentheses in order to make the meaning obvious. Moreover, it is necessary to enclose the whole conditional arithmetic expression in parentheses whenever it appears within a larger expression.

The *conditional proposition* has the form

$$\textbf{if } B \textbf{ then } B_1 \textbf{ else } B_2$$

where B_1 and B_2 stand for Boolean expressions. The evaluation of the conditional proposition is the same as that of the conditional arithmetic expression if the following replacements are made. Replace arithmetic expression by proposition (or Boolean expression), and E_1 and E_2 by B_1 and B_2.

A conditional arithmetic expression can itself appear in place of an arithmetic expression or as a component of such an expression. Conditional expressions that are components of comparisons must be enclosed in parentheses.

EXAMPLES

$$A := \textbf{if } i < 0 \textbf{ then } r \textbf{ else } 3;$$

A is assigned the value of r if i is negative, and the value 3 if i is nonnegative.

$$\textbf{for } i := \textbf{if } n \wedge v \textbf{ then } 1 \textbf{ else } 0 \textbf{ step} \cdots$$

The initial value of i is 1 or 0 depending on whether $n \wedge v$ has value **true** or **false**. Hence, both n and v are Boolean variables.

$$(\textbf{if } a \textbf{ then } b \textbf{ else } c) = d$$

This is a comparison; a is a Boolean variable while b, c, and d assume numerical values.

(**if** a **then** (**if** U **then** m **else** n) **else** c) $= d$

This is again a comparison: a and U are Boolean; m, n, c, and d are real or integer variables.

8.4. EXAMPLES

Let $f_0, f_1, \ldots, f_m$ be the values of the members of a Sturm sequence that belong to the polynomial $p(x)$.

$$p(x) = f_0$$
$$p'(x) = f_1 .$$

It is required to establish the number of changes of sign. From the properties of Sturm sequences it follows that

$$f_m \neq 0$$

and for $v = 1, 2, \ldots, m - 1$

$$f_{v-1} = -f_{v+1} \text{ whenever } f_v = 0.$$

Moreover,

$$f_0 = 0$$

may be excluded.

Under these assumptions the following piece of program determines the number of changes of sign.

```
if f[0] ≠ 0 then
  begin
    w := 0;
    for i := 0 step 1 until m − 1 do
        begin if f[i] ≥ 0 ≡ f[i + 1] < 0 then w := w + 1 end
  end
```

9 DESIGNATIONAL EXPRESSIONS

The possible applications of the jump statement can be extended by admitting into the language elements which represent labels. In particular, the jump target can be specified by one of a set of labels. The choice of one of the components of a set of labels does not take place until the execution of the jump statement.

9.1. DEFINITION OF DESIGNATIONAL EXPRESSION

A jump statement interrupts the static sequence of a program by specifying which statement is to be executed next, and that statement we call the *jump target*. The jump statement specifies the jump target by designating the label attached to the jump target (cf. Section 6.1). In the general case the jump statement indicates the jump target by means of a *designational expression* which is a construct representing a label. The "value" of a designational expression is a label; in fact, a label is the most elementary form of a designational expression. Below we discuss other kinds of designational expressions.

9.2. THE SWITCH DECLARATION

A *switch* is a set of labels which can be placed at the disposal of a jump. A switch is declared by designating a name and assigning designational expressions to all the components. The declaration is introduced by the symbol

switch

and uses the assignment symbol to assign the designational expressions.

EXAMPLES

switch *alpha* := *C*1, *B*5, *A*3, *Postmortem*;
switch *ex* := *A*1, *B*2, *C*3, *D*4, *E*5, *F*6, *G*7;

The designational expressions on the right side of the assignment symbol are

53

separated by commas. The sequence establishes an internal enumeration, beginning with 1 for the leftmost component, which is referred to by the switch call.

9.3. THE SWITCH CALL

A component of a switch can be called by a jump statement lying within the scope of validity of the switch declaration. In this case, instead of a label, the jump statement contains a designational expression consisting of the name of the switch and a subscript expression enclosed in brackets. This designational expression is called a *switch designator*.

EXAMPLES

We refer to the examples in Section 9.2

$$\textbf{go to } alpha[2];$$

The switch designator is *alpha*[2]; the jump target is the statement labeled *B5*.

$$\textbf{go to } ex[3 \times i - 1];$$

If $i = 1$ then the label is *B2* and if $i = 2$ the label is *E5*.

It is clear that the subscript expression is intended to be an integral number. This integer is obtained exactly as if the expression were the subscript of a subscripted variable (cf. Section 4.2). The subscript expression assumes one of the values of the internal numbering of the labels appearing in the declaration. Otherwise the jump is not defined. The jump target is the statement whose label appears in the switch declaration in the position indicated by the subscript expression. Moreover, the jump statement must lie inside of the scope of validity of the label specified by the designational expression. Otherwise, the jump is not defined.

9.4. NESTING OF SWITCHES

In full ALGOL 60 a designational expression may take the place of a label on the right-hand side of a switch declaration. For this reason switches can be nested.

EXAMPLE

```
begin switch s1 := L1, L2, L3; integer a;
   D; D; ...; D;
   S; S; ...; S;
      begin switch s2 := N1, s1[a], N3;
         D; D; ...; D;
         S; S; ...; S
      end;
   S; S; ...; S
end
```

If a is assigned a value before entering the innermost block, then the declaration of $s2$ roughly resembles a dynamic array declaration (cf. Section 7.4). This is true in the sense that $s1$ and a are nonlocal to the innermost block and a has previously been assigned a value. Thus, $s1[a]$ clearly designates a label which is fixed throughout the innermost block.

However, this similarity between an array declaration and a switch declaration is not required. The following example gives a valid program where this similarity does not exist.

EXAMPLE

Consider the following program

```
begin integer i, j;
    switch A := L1, L2, L3, L4;
    switch B := N1, N2, A[i];
    D; D; ...; D;
    S; S; ...; S;
    go to B[j];
    S; S; ...; S
end
```

The jump target of the jump statement is clearly specified by the label $N1$ if $j = 1$ and by $N2$ if $j = 2$. If $j = 3$, then the jump target is specified by one of the labels $L1$, $L2$, $L3$, or $L4$ depending on whether i is respectively 1, 2, 3, or 4. If $j = 3$, then the jump is not defined unless i has been assigned a numerical value before the jump statement is executed. Hence the jump is defined only if

$$j = 1 \text{ or } 2$$

or if

$$j = 3 \text{ and } i = 1, 2, 3, \text{ or } 4.$$

9.5. ANOTHER FORM OF DESIGNATIONAL EXPRESSION

In full ALGOL 60 a designational expression also can be subjected to a condition. The *conditional designational expression* has the form

$$\text{if } B \text{ then } T_1 \text{ else } T_2$$

where T_1 and T_2 stand for designational expressions. The evaluation of the conditional designational expression is like that of the conditional arithmetic expression (cf. Section 8.3). The conditional designational expression has the value of T_1 whenever the value of B is **true** and of T_2 if the value of B is **false**. Moreover, T_2 may be a conditional designational expression, whereas T_1 may be a conditional designational expression only if it is enclosed in parentheses.

EXAMPLE

$$\text{go to if } a \geq 0 \text{ then } ALPHA \text{ else } OMEGA$$

Here the jump target is the statement labeled $ALPHA$ if $a \geq 0$; otherwise, the jump target is the statement labeled $OMEGA$.

9.6. EXAMPLE

Let the function

$$y = f(x)$$

defined in the interval

$$0 \leq x < 6$$

be composed of continuous functions

$$f(x) = \begin{array}{ll} f_1(x) & \text{for} \quad 0 \leq x < 2 \\ f_2(x) & \text{for} \quad 2 \leq x < 4 \\ f_3(x) & \text{for} \quad 4 \leq x < 6 \end{array}$$

where

$$f_1(x) = -x + 2.5$$
$$f_2(x) = 2 - 1.5(x - 3)^2$$
$$f_3(x) = (x/2) - 1.5 .$$

The following program uses a switch to evaluate the function at an arbitrary value of x.

```
        begin real x;
          switch function := f1, f2, f3, Z;
          read(x);
          go to function[if abs(x − 3) ≤ 3 then entier (x/2 + 1) else 4];
  f1:     print(−x + 2.5); go to Z;
  f2:     print(2 − 1.5 × (x − 3) × (x − 3)); go to Z;
  f3:     print(x/2 − 1.5);
  Z:   end
```

Here the statement labeled Z is empty and has no effect on the program. It is called a *dummy statement* and it serves to place a label. This is an example in the proper use of the dummy statement.

10 PROCEDURES

Statements or blocks which describe certain frequently appearing computational processes may appear repeatedly in the same program although with different names used to designate some of the quantities involved. If such is the fact, it is appropriate to give a name to the entire portion of program, whether it is a statement or a block, by means of a special declaration, and to summon the piece of program with this name. These pieces of programs are called procedures.

It is advantageous to formulate as procedures those computational rules which are used in different programs or whose later re-use is foreseen; this is especially true of the basic methods of numerical analysis. The quantities appearing in a procedure which are accessible from without (the so-called parameters) must be precisely regulated in every single case.

The procedure is the most comprehensive linguistic component of ALGOL. Above all, its composition appears to be very complicated; however, the reader should not be intimidated by this. In each case the procedure is not more complicated than the computational process which it describes.

10.1. THE PROCEDURE DECLARATION

The procedure declaration is a component of the declaration part of a block and it is subject to the same rules concerning its scope of validity as is the declaration of any other quantity (cf. Section 7.2).

The name under which the procedure should later be called is designated in the procedure declaration. With this name the procedure becomes a quantity in the sense of Section 7.2.

The quantity *procedure* is used as an abbreviation for a simple or compound statement or for a block. This piece of program, called the *body* of the procedure, is to be written in the procedure declaration. If the body is a block, then the quantities declared therein are local with respect to the body and are unavailable from without. Each label attached to a statement within the procedure body is also a local quantity. In what follows no more will be said about local quantities.

EXAMPLE 1

In the block

```
begin integer i; real s;
  s := 0;
  for i := 1 step 1 until n do
    s := s + a[i, i];
  Trace := s
end
```

the quantities i and s are local, and *Trace*, n, and a nonlocal.

The nonlocal quantities appearing inside the body, we call *parameters* of the procedure. In case the body is not a block only nonlocal quantities can appear in it apart from labels. The procedure declaration must contain clear specifications about the handling of those parameters appearing in the body which are used with mutable names. In particular, the procedure declaration must contain some regulations, for instance, about the manner of later use of the procedure, about the kinds of parameters appearing in the procedure and their exchange in the actual procedure call. These criteria are established for the entire scope of validity of the procedure declaration.

The standpoint from which these rules are to be made is presented in Sections 10.1.1, 10.1.2, and 10.1.3. The form of the procedure declaration is discussed in Section 10.1.4.

10.1.1. GLOBAL AND FORMAL PARAMETERS

A parameter of a procedure can be of either of two kinds:

(a) The declaration of the quantity under consideration lies outside of the procedure declaration in the same or in a dominant block. The scope of validity of the declaration of this quantity contains the declaration of the procedure.

In using the procedure this parameter cannot be set with a mutable name. This quantity is called a *global parameter* of the procedure and does not appear in the procedure call at all.

(b) A quantity (or an expression) entering as a parameter should be able to change when the procedure is used repeatedly. Such a quantity (or expression) can only be definitively established at the summon of the procedure. In the body of the procedure declaration there must appear a representative, a "formal" element, whose only mission is to hold the place of this quantity (or expression). This place holding element is called a *formal parameter* of the procedure. The element which enters in the procedure call to take the place of the formal parameter, we call an *actual quantity* (or *actual expression*) or, in general, *actual parameter*.

EXAMPLE 2

Let the object of a program be to operate on vectors and matrices of fixed dimension n. If from time to time within the program it is necessary to calculate the traces of different matrices, then the computation of the trace (cf. Example 1 above) is formulated as a procedure. Suitably, the array of the matrix A is to be introduced as a formal, the dimension number n as a global parameter.

In this case the program contains among other things the following components in the suggested sequence:

Type declaration for the quantity n;

. . .

Declaration of a procedure *Trace* with formal parameter A;

. . .

Assignment of a value to n;

. . .

Assignment of a value to an array B;

. . .

Call of procedure *Trace* with actual parameter B;

. . .

Assignment of a value to an array C;

. . .

Call of procedure *Trace* with actual parameter C;

. . .

The type declaration and the value assignment corresponding to the global parameter n can also take place in a dominant block. In the procedure calls the actual parameter is at one time B and at another time C.

On account of its provisional character the formal parameter in different respects occupies an exceptional position among the quantities. An arbitrary name may be used to designate a formal parameter, but no declaration is necessary to do this. When the same name already appears in different parts of the program no allusion is made to the declarations and these declarations are meaningless to the formal parameter. Instead of a declaration a single *specification* is used indicating the kind of formal parameter (simple variable, array,[1] procedure, label, or switch) and its type.

---

[1] The quantity "array", characterized solely by a name, denotes the collection of all the declared components of a subscripted variable (cf. Sections 4.2 and 4.2.1).

10.1.2. CHARACTERIZATION OF FORMAL PARAMETERS

During the run of the procedure formal parameters can operate in very different ways. They can introduce in the procedure values, quantities, or computational instructions (algorithms) as arguments; they can get values of results out of the procedure; and they can set jump targets for side exits out of the procedure. We distinguish the formal parameters according to these points of view into

arguments
results
exits

10.1.2.1. Arguments. Arguments serve to introduce into the procedure values assigned to certain quantities previous to the procedure call, or computational rules. A rule of computation can be brought into the procedure in case the computation is defined by means of another procedure declaration.[1]

Formal simple variables, formal arrays, and formal procedures can act as arguments.

EXAMPLE 3

Approximations to the Fourier coefficients of the function $f(x)$ defined in an interval $[a, b]$

$$a_k = \frac{1}{n} \sum_{i=0}^{2n-1} f\left(a + i \cdot \frac{b-a}{2n}\right) \cdot cos\left(\frac{2\pi k}{b-a} \cdot \left(a + i \cdot \frac{b-a}{2n}\right)\right)$$

$$b_k = \frac{1}{n} \sum_{i=0}^{2n-1} f\left(a + i \cdot \frac{b-a}{2n}\right) \cdot sin\left(\frac{2\pi k}{b-a} \cdot \left(a + i \cdot \frac{b-a}{2n}\right)\right)$$

are computed in the following procedure body.

```
begin integer i, k; real p, q, r, s;
   p := (b − a)/(2 × n);
   q := 6.283185307/(b − a);
   for k := 0 step 1 until n − 1 do
      begin
         r := k × q; s := 0;
         for i := 0 step 1 until 2 × n − 1 do
            s := s + fct(a + i × p) × cs(r × (a + i × p));
         ab[k] := s/n
      end
end
```

---

[1] In full ALGOL 60 a computational rule can also be brought in as an expression in case it is solely an expression. See Chapter 11.

The quantities a, b, n, fct, and cs appear as arguments; in fact

a, b, n appear as formal simple variables and

fct, cs appear as formal procedures.

If the values of the function $f(x)$ are already calculated at the points

$$a + i \cdot \frac{b - a}{2n} \quad \text{for} \quad i = 1, 2, \ldots, 2n - 1;$$

then the iterated statements of the two loops are altered by replacing the statement

$$s := s + fct(a + i \times p) \times cs(r \times (a + i \times p));$$

by

$$s := s + f[i] \times cs(r \times (a + i \times p));$$

where f denotes a formal array found among the arguments of the procedure.

Formal simple variables can be used as arguments in two different ways.

(a) *Call by value.* Normally, a formal simple variable serves to bring into the procedure the value of the corresponding actual expression[1] (not the expression itself). Directly at the procedure call the formal quantity is assigned the value of the corresponding actual parameter *once*. Subsequently the formal simple variable is handled as a local quantity although no declaration concerning this quantity is present. In addition to the specification concerning the type of variable, the name of the formal quantity is listed in the "value part" appearing at the head of the procedure (cf. Section 10.1.4).

(b) *Call by name.*[2] On the other hand, a formal simple variable may serve to refer simply to a variable name. In this case the formal parameter is literally a place holder. At each place of the body in which it appears the formal simple variable stands for the actual simple variable. If a formal simple variable does not appear in the value part, then the corresponding actual parameter is to be called by name.

EXAMPLE 4

The procedure body below can be used to evaluate a polynomial of degree n

$$p(x) = \sum_{i=0}^{n} a_i x^i$$

at a point x.

---

[1] It is clear that the actual expression can also consist of only one variable or one number.

[2] In full ALGOL 60 the call by name is more general. See Chapter 11.

```
begin integer i; real t;
    t := 0;
    for i := n step −1 until 0 do
        t := t × x + a[i];
    p := t
end
```

Here i and t are local quantities; x, a, and p are formal parameters; and x and a are arguments. It is clear that the evaluation of the polynomial according to Horner's scheme is executed at a fixed value of the variable x. Therefore, the formal simple variable x requires a call by value.

If at the procedure call the actual parameter corresponding to x is

$$u \cdot u + v \cdot v,$$

then the call of the procedure has the following effect

```
begin integer i; real t;

    real x;
    x := u × u + v × v;

    t := 0;
    for i := n step −1 until 0 do
        t := t × x + a[i];
    p := t
end
```

In general, failure to distinguish between call by value and call by name may even lead to wrong assignments of values to the results, especially if the call by name makes good sense.

EXAMPLE 5

A procedure is to be constructed which counts up by one any given simple variable under the assumption that such a counting process occurs frequently in a certain program.

If the formal simple variable to be counted up is x, then the body of the procedure may be expressed simply by

```
x := x + 1
```

Calling x by value does not yield the desired result. If x is called by value and at a procedure call the actual parameter corresponding to x is c, then the value of e is assigned to the local quantity x. The incremental value of x is not accessible outside of the procedure body since it has no connection with the actual parameter c. This example is further discussed in Section 10.1.2.2.

A *formal array* can also be used as an argument in two ways. Whether it is called by value or called by name the formal quantity is an array identifier which can only be associated to an actual quantity which is itself an array identifier. The formal array and the corresponding actual array must have the same number of subscript positions.

(a) *Call by value.* If a formal array is called by value then the array identifier appears in the value part and in the specification part at the head of the procedure (cf. Section 10.1.4). Directly at procedure call each component of the formal array is assigned the value of the corresponding component of the actual array; that is, the component of the actual array with the same combination of subscripts. Subsequently the formal array is treated as a local quantity although no declaration is present.

(b) *Call by name.* A formal array may also be called by name. In this case, directly at procedure call, the name of the corresponding actual array replaces the name of the formal array at each place where the latter appears.

It is clear that the actual array corresponding to the formal array must be assigned values at each of the components used in the procedure body.

As an illustration consider the procedure discussed in Example 4 above. Assume that x, n, and a are formal parameters used as arguments, their corresponding actual parameters are z, k, and b. Furthermore, x and n are called by value.

The effect of the procedure when a is called by value is the following

```
begin integer i; real t;
   ┌─────────────────────────────┐
   │ real x; integer n;          │
   │ x := z; n := k;             │
   │    begin array a[0:n];      │
   │       for i := 1 step 1 until n do │
   │          a[i] := b[i];      │
   └─────────────────────────────┘
          t := 0;
          for i := n step −1 until 0 do
             t := t × x + a[i];
          p := t
       end
end
```

The effect of the procedure call when a is called by name is the following

begin integer i; **real** t;

real x; **integer** n;

$x := z$; $n := k$;

$t := 0$;
for $i := n$ **step** -1 **until** 0 **do**

$t := t \times x + b[i]$;

$p := t$
end

Call by name and call by value for simple variable and array arguments show an essential and practically important difference: The values of the actual quantities can be changed by the procedure if and only if the quantity is called by name, with all the advantages and disadvantages of such a mechanism. One advantage of the call by name is that storage is saved; this is especially important for arrays.

Finally among the arguments of a procedure there may be *formal procedure* identifiers designating arbitrary procedures. The identifier *fct* in Example 3, which stands for the function to be analyzed, belongs to this class of arguments. In every place of the text of the procedure body where a formal procedure identifier appears, the computing rule defined by the actual argument (which must be the identifier of a properly declared procedure) is to be executed.

10.1.2.2. Results. Formal simple variables and formal arrays can act as results. Results serve to take out of the procedure values assigned to quantities inside of the procedure. Again, formal parameters acting as results refer simply to a name of a variable[1] or to an array name; it follows that only simple variables or arrays can appear as corresponding actual quantities.

In Example 1 the formal simple variable *Trace*, in Example 3 the formal array *ab*, and in Example 4 the formal simple variable p are results.

It is evident that a formal array or a formal simple variable may appear as argument and result at the same time. It is likewise true in this case that neither formal quantity can be called by value. In Example 5 the formal simple variable x acts as argument and result. Formal parameters of this mixed kind

---

[1] In full ALGOL 60 a formal simple variable acting as result can also refer to a subscripted variable. See Chapter 11.

which generally will lead to changes in the actual quantities, we call *transients*. Arrays are frequently treated as transients due to considerations of storage capacity.

10.1.2.3. Exits. Formal labels and formal switches act as exits. The purpose of exits is to bring in jump targets which are to be used as side exits leading out of the procedure. The actual parameter corresponding to a formal label can only be a designation expression. The label represented by the designational expression is obtained at each place where the formal label appears, the actual jump target is obtained by evaluating at that place the actual designational expression.

A formal switch identifier is treated like a formal procedure parameter (cf. Section 10.1.2.1).

10.1.3. FUNCTION PROCEDURES AND PROPER PROCEDURES

From given pieces of program, procedures can be derived *either* in the form of function procedures *or* in the form of proper procedures.

The body of a *function procedure* must be so constructed that each time the piece of program is run there results one numerical value or logical value which is assigned to the procedure quantity. This procedure quantity looks like a simple variable named by the function identifier and may appear only on the left hand side of assignment statements.

In accordance with common mathematical practice we assume that a function procedure obviously may not contain jumps leading outside of the body, and assignments of values to nonlocal quantities with the exception of assignments of values to the procedure quantity itself. Thus, a function procedure can only have arguments as formal parameters.

The assignment of the value of the result to the procedure quantity must not depend on conditions through which the assignment could be prevented.

If any one of these requirements is not satisfied, then the procedure can be set up only as a *proper procedure*.

The way in which a procedure is set up and used is a fixed characteristic of the procedure and is established directly in the declaration by means of the introducing symbols. The declaration of functions is introduced by the symbols

real procedure
integer procedure
Boolean procedure

according to the type of the resulting value. The declaration of the proper procedure begins with the symbol

procedure

only. No resulting value can be attached to the procedure identifier.

10.1.4. THE PROCEDURE HEAD

All necessary assertions about the formal parameters and the use of the procedure are contained in the *head* of the procedure declaration. Invariably the head stands on top of the body. Head and body constitute the complete procedure declaration. The head consists of five parts:

    (1) Introductory symbol
    (2) Procedure name
    (3) List of formal parameters
    (4) Value part
    (5) Specification part

The following comments refer to them:

(1) The introductory symbol determines the later use of the procedure (cf. Section 10.1.3).

(2) The procedure name can be chosen almost arbitrarily. The only valid restriction is the general limitation concerning some reserved names (cf. Section 1.3).

(3) The names of all the formal parameters are called in the formal parameter list. This list is enclosed in parentheses. The comma serves as the general separation symbol. Thus, in Example 6 on page 68, the formal parameter list reads

$$(a, n)$$

In some cases it is desirable to give an idea about the nature of the formal parameters. This is accomplished by replacing the separation symbol "," by the following sequence

$$) \text{ any sequence of letters} : ($$

Hence in Example 6 the parameter list could be written

$$(a) \text{ order} : (n)$$

Here the comma between a and n was replaced by

$$) \text{ order} : ($$

It is clear that the leftmost of the elements in the formal parameter list cannot be preceded by a sequence of this kind.

In the sequel we shall use, if necessary, the special separators) result : (and) exit : (to separate arguments from results and results from exits.

(4) The formal parameter list is followed, if necessary, by the *value part*. This is introduced by the symbol

value

Following this symbol are listed the names of all those formal parameters which are to be called by value (cf. Section 10.1.2.1). The comma serves to separate the elements of the list. If no formal parameter is called by value, then the value part is empty and the symbol **value** drops out.

(5) The value part is followed by the *specification part* of the procedure declaration. Here are listed the names of the formal parameters grouped according to the kind of quantities they represent, where each name appears exactly once. The formal parameters are distinguished according to kind into simple variables, arrays,[1] and functions of type **real**, **integer**, or **Boolean**, as well as proper procedures, labels, and switches.

The individual lists are introduced with the symbols

> **real**
> **integer**
> **Boolean**
> **array** or **real array**
> **integer array**
> **Boolean array**
> **real procedure**
> **integer procedure**
> **Boolean procedure**
> **procedure**
> **label**
> **switch**

An element within a list is separated from the other elements of the list by a comma. In turn each of the lists is separated from the others by a semicolon. If a list is empty, then the corresponding symbol also drops out.

Consider the sequence which consists of the introducing symbol, the name of the procedure, and the formal parameter list as an item. This item, the value part, and the specification part, are separated from one another by a semicolon. If, say, the value part is empty, then only one semicolon separates the first item from the specification part. Head and body are separated by a semicolon.

EXAMPLE 6

It is required to determine the trace of an *n*-rowed square matrix A with real components a_{ik} by means of a function procedure. A single numerical value

$$Trace = \sum_{i=1}^{n} a_{ii}$$

appears as the result. The determination of the trace is not subject to any restrictive conditions; therefore, the process is easily formulated as a function procedure. The body of the function procedure must be a block because it uses two local quantities which do not appear outside of the procedure, a loop variable and a summation variable.

---

[1] No subscript bounds are allowed.

The complete procedure declaration reads (cf. Examples 1 and 2):

```
real procedure Trace(a, n);
    value n;
    integer n; array a;
    begin integer i; real s;
        s := 0;
        for i := 1 step 1 until n do
            s := s + a[i, i];
        Trace := s
    end
```

EXAMPLE 7

In connection with Example 5, a proper procedure can be formulated to count up a simple variable by 1. The declaration reads

```
procedure count up (x);
    integer x;
        x := x + 1
```

EXAMPLE 8

In a program the extraction of a square root frequently appears tied in to a branching of the program depending upon the sign of the radicand. Therefore, it is worthwhile to combine the branching and root extraction in a procedure.

The declaration of the procedure reads:

```
procedure ROOTEX(x) result : (y) exit : (imag);
    value x;
    real x, y; label imag;

    if x ≥ 0 then
        y := sqrt(x)
    else
    begin
        y := sqrt(abs(x));
        go to imag
    end
```

EXAMPLE 9

The procedure body constructed in Example 3 is built into a complete procedure declaration by using the following head:

procedure *Fourco*(*a*, *b*, *n*, *fct*, *cs*) result : (*ab*);
    value *a*, *b*, *n*;
    real *a*, *b*;
    integer *n*;
    array *ab*;
    real procedure *fct*, *cs*;

```
begin integer i, k; real p, q, r, s;
    p := (b − a)/(2 × n);
    q := 6.283185307/(b − a);
    for k := 0 step 1 until n − 1 do
        begin
            r := k × q; s := 0;
            for i := 0 step 1 until 2 × n − 1 do
                s := s + fct(a + i × p) × cs(r × (a + i × p));
            ab[k] := s/n
        end
end
```

10.2. THE PROCEDURE CALL

A procedure can be summoned by its name any time within the scope of validity of its declaration. Immediately following the procedure name appears a list of actual parameters which has the same number of entries and the same arrangement as does the list of formal parameters. Quantities or expressions can appear as list elements. Elementwise they are arranged in the same order in which the formal parameters are listed in the declaration.

A program is meaningful only if in filling the list of actual parameters all limitations concerning the character of the formal parameters are observed (cf. Section 10.1.2). Thus, for instance, an actual expression can be included in the list of actual parameters if the corresponding formal parameter is a simple variable argument called by value.

In the run of the program after the formal parameters are replaced by the actual parameters, the procedure body is inserted at the place of call. It is obvious that both the parameter replacement and the insertion of the procedure body must not lead to any inconsistencies.

To that end the quantities which occur in the list of the actual parameters must satisfy the following conditions:

(1) Type and kind of each actual parameter must coincide with the specification of the corresponding formal parameter.

(2) Values must previously be assigned to the simple variables and arrays appearing as arguments.

(3) The declaration of an actual array must agree with the corresponding formal array concerning the number of subscript positions.

(4) The declaration of an actual array must cover all components called during the course of the procedure.

A global parameter used in a procedure declaration refers to a quantity declared in the same or a dominant block. The procedure can be called at any place within the scope of validity of the procedure declaration and the global parameter corresponds to the one used in the procedure declaration. Therefore, in the following program the global parameter used in the procedure call is the one declared in the dominant block.

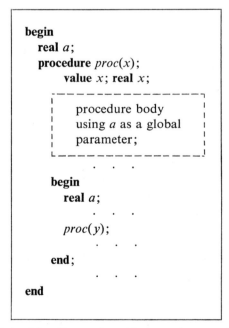

Any other use of the identifier a is subject to the usual rules concerning declarations (cf. Section 7.2).

Global parameters may be used to advantage under any circumstance where the name of such a parameter can be held fixed within a block. For instance, in a piece of program matrices may be of the same order, say n; the variable *n* could be treated as a global parameter in any procedure dealing with matrices in this piece of program.

Global parameters are especially useful if the values of some quantities in the procedure are to be made available in successive calls.

Further examples in the use of global parameters in procedures are found in Chapter 11.

10.2.1. CALL OF THE FUNCTION PROCEDURE

We make a distinction between function procedure and function designator. The function procedure with the name *Bessel* yields the function designator *Bessel(i, x)*. The function designator *Bessel(i, x)* can appear in an expression provided the function procedure *Bessel* has been previously established by means of a procedure declaration. To the expression containing it, the function designator *Bessel(i, x)* represents the value which will be assigned to the function quantity *Bessel* at the execution of the procedure.

A function designator can appear only in an expression. The corresponding procedure is called during the course of the evaluation of the expression. After the procedure is run, the evaluation of the expression is continued with the value obtained, as the value of the procedure quantity, by executing the procedure.

The requirements for function procedures listed in Section 10.1.3 ensure that execution of the function procedure causes no side effects. The only resulting value is always assigned to the procedure quantity itself.

Thus, it is possible to call the function procedure *Trace* declared in Example 6 by means of a function designator *Trace(V, E)* appearing in arbitrary expressions, e.g.:

$$z := (Trace(x, r) + Trace(y, s))/(r + s);$$

10.2.2. CALL OF THE PROPER PROCEDURE

The call of a proper procedure takes place by means of a *procedure statement*. It consists exclusively of the procedure name and the list of actual parameters. At the call the procedure statement is replaced by the declared piece of program. This piece of program can be left by means of a jump statement leading to another place in the program (that is, the program that contains the call). Otherwise, the statement next executed immediately after the procedure statement is the statement next following the call in the text of the program.

The effect of the procedure in the program is that those quantities which are results in the list of actual parameters as well as nonlocal parameters (if such be the case) are assigned values. Moreover, the course of the program may be influenced by jump statements whose jump targets appear as actual or global parameters.

Therefore, in order to be able to survey the effect of the execution of a procedure the whole procedure body must be examined for value assignments and jump statements. Assuming that the nonlocal parameters are not affected, the user is relieved of this work by a subdivision of the formal parameters as suggested in Section 10.1.2. When this subdivision is made in the procedure declaration (cf. Section 10.1.4 and Example 8) thereupon the user may rely on the fact that the values of quantities associated only to arguments do not alter during the course of the procedure and only the quantities appearing as exits act as jump targets of jumps leading out through a side exit.

In addition, it is to be recommended to write in a procedure declaration appropriate comments about the appearance and effect of global parameters.

The procedure *ROOTEX* declared in Example 8 can possibly be called by the following procedure statement

$$ROOTEX(a) \text{ result} : (b) \text{ exit} : (c1);$$

provided that b is of type real and $c1$ is a label.

The procedure *count up* declared in Example 7 can possibly be called by the following procedure statement

> *count up* (i);

Here i is of type integer.

10.3. EXAMPLE

As a final example of the application of a function procedure consider a method to evaluate the definite integral of a given integrand between given limits. The method begins with the simple trapezoidal and rectangular approximations and improves recursively the values thus obtained by passing to an approximation of higher order with a simultaneous doubling of the number of subdivisions.[1] Since it is desirable that this procedure be declared independently of a special integrand function, the integrand function itself must appear as a formal function procedure, that is, it enters into the procedure "Romberg integration" as a formal parameter. Furthermore, it is clear that the upper and lower limits of the definite integral as well as the order of approximation desired enter as formal parameters.

---

[1] Romberg integration. A detailed account of this method is found in F. L. Bauer, *La méthode d'integration numérique de Romberg. Colloque sur l'analyse numérique*, Mons 1961; and E. Stiefel, "Altes und Neues über numerische Quadratur", *ZAMM*, 41 (1961), pp. 408–13.

```
real procedure Rombergint(fct, a, b, ord);
    value a, b, ord;
    integer ord;
    real a, b;
    real procedure fct;
    begin
      ord := entier((ord + 1)/2);
      begin
        integer f, h, j, n;
        real l, m, s;
        array U, T[1:ord];
        l := b − a;
        T[1] := (fct(a) + fct(b))/2;
        U[1] := fct((a + b)/2);
        f := n := 1;
      for h := 2 step 1 until ord − 1 do
        begin
          n := 2 × n; s := 0; m := l/(2 × n);
          for j := 1 step 2 until 2 × n − 1 do
            s := s + fct(a + j × m);
          U[h] := s/n;
          T[h] := (T[h − 1] + U[h − 1])/2;
          f := 1;
          for j := h − 1 step −1 until 1 do
            begin
              f := 4 × f;
              T[j] := T[j + 1] + (T[j + 1] − T[j])/(f − 1);
              U[j] := U[j + 1] + (U[j + 1] − U[j])/(f − 1)
            end
        end;
      if ord > 1 then
        begin
          T[2] := (U[1] + T[1])/2;
          T[1] := T[2] + (T[2] − T[1])/(4 × f − 1)
        end;
      Rombergint := T[1] × l
    end
  end
```

In the following piece of program the Romberg procedure is used to determine

$$a = \int_{x_1}^{x_2} \sin(x)dx$$

within an approximation value of order 10.

> **if** $x[2] > x[1]$ **then**
> $a := Rombergint(sin, x[1], x[2], 10);$

If later in the run of the program a appears only once, say in

$$w := (7 \times a - 3 \times c)/sin(y \times y);$$

then it can be computed directly at this point

> **if** $x[2] > x[1]$ **then**
> $w := (7 \times Rombergint(sin, x[1], x[2], 10) - 3 \times c)/sin(y \times y);$

III ALGORITHMIC LANGUAGE ALGOL ADVANCED CONCEPTS

A powerful subset of ALGOL[1] has been developed in the previous Parts I and II. This subset is sufficient for most applications, especially for the beginner. There exist, however, advanced concepts in ALGOL which under specific circumstances and with proper care might prove to be useful. In Chapter 11 are discussed uses of expressions called by name. Procedures calling themselves are treated in Chapter 12.

---

[1] We tried to make this subset correspond with the IFIP subset.

11 USES OF EXPRESSIONS CALLED BY NAME

11.1 EXPRESSIONS AS ARGUMENTS

In full ALGOL, as remarked already in Chapter 10, a computational rule cannot only be brought into a procedure by means of another procedure, but also by means of an expression (in case it is solely an expression) replacing a formal simple variable under a name call. In this case the actual expression acts as argument.

Thus in Example 4, Section 10.1.2.1, x could be called by name and still an expression could be the actual parameter. However, it is unwise to do so because the actual expression is needlessly evaluated many times.

There are cases, however, where the call by name of an expression provides procedures more flexibly.

EXAMPLE 1

The components of the subscripted variables a_i constitute an ordered set of numbers. Subsequences of this sequence, defined by means of special rules of formation, are to be summed up by means of a general procedure, applicable for arbitrary rules of formation.

The procedure body may be expressed by

```
begin real s;
    i := 1; s := 0;
L1:s := s + a[u];
    i := i + 1;
    if u ≤ v then go to L1 else SUM := s
end
```

Here s is a local quantity, i and a are global parameters, and u and v are formal parameters which are not introduced by a call by name.

77

The meaning of the value assigned by the procedure to the result SUM can be learned from the following table. The first line indicates the formal quantities; each of the other lines indicates a set of corresponding actual quantities.

u	v	SUM	
i	n	$a_1 + a_2 + a_3 + \cdots + a_n$	
$2 \times i - 1$	m	$a_1 + a_3 + a_5 + \cdots + a_z$	$z \leq m$
$i \times (i + 1)/2$	r	$a_1 + a_3 + a_6 + a_{10} + a_{15} + \cdots + a_z$	$z \leq r$

If the formal parameter u is erroneously introduced by a call by value, then the procedure is meaningless.

Note that by using a formal simple variable as argument the call by value introduces the value of an expression; whereas the call by name introduces a computational rule defined by an expression without the need of a declaration.

EXAMPLE 2

In connection with Example 1, a proper procedure can be formulated to obtain different sums of squares of a set of numbers a_i from

array $a[1 : z]$.

In so doing the quantities i, z, and a are to be treated as nonlocal parameters. The declaration reads

```
procedure SUM(u) result : (RES);
  integer u; real RES;

  begin real s, h;
    s := 0;
    i := 1;
L1: h := a[u] × a[u];
    s := s + h;
    i := i + 1;
    if u ≤ z then go to L1;
    RES := s
  end
```

Again, this procedure can be used to sum squares over any range of the subscript i determined by the successive values the parameter u assumes as a function of i. The actual parameter corresponding to u has to be an expression that explicitly contains i or depends on i in some other way.

It would even be possible to list the hereto global parameter i in the formal parameter list. This would allow to point to any variable acting as summation index in an actual expression corresponding to u by introducing the actual summation index through a name replacement for i (the so-called *Jensen device*).[1]

In such a sophisticated use of the name call of an expression some variables (the global or formal parameter i in the example) act as bound variables in the procedure statement.

EXAMPLE 3

The procedure SUM declared in Example 2 can be used to calculate the values

$$s_1 = \sum_{j=1}^{j=n} a_{jj}^2$$

$$s_2 = \sum_{j=1}^{j=n} \sum_{k=1}^{k=j-1} a_{jk}^2$$

$$s_3 = 2 \cdot s_2 + s_1$$

for a given real symmetric matrix A with element a_{jk}. The matrix elements

$$a_{jk} \quad \text{with} \quad j \geq k,$$

that is, the elements of the "lower triangle" including the main diagonal are given as components of single subscript variables $a[i]$, where the correspondence $i(j, k)$ is established by

$$i = (j \cdot (j - 1))/2 + k$$

The program is expressed as follows

```
begin integer n, z;
   read(n)
   z := n × (n + 1)/2;
   begin integer i;
         real s1, s2, s3;
         array a[1 : z];

         procedure SUM(u) result : (RES);
            integer u; real RES;
            begin real s, h;
               s := 0; i := 1;
         L1: h := a[u] × a[u];
               s := s + h; i := i + 1;
               if u ≤ z then go to L1;
               RES := s
            end;
```

[1] See procedure *Innerproduct* in Section 5.4.2 of the ALGOL Report.

```
        for i := 1 step 1 until z do
            read(a[i]);
        SUM(i × (i + 1)/2) result : (s1);
        SUM(i) result : (s2);
        s2 := s2 − s1;
        s3 := 2 × s2 + s1;
        print(s1, s2, s3)
    end
end
```

11.2 SUBSCRIPTED VARIABLES AS RESULTS

In full ALGOL 60 expressions which produce meaningful replacements of variables on the left part of an assignment statement may also be entered under call by name, acting as results. This extends to subscripted variables, the actual parameters corresponding to a formal simple variable used as a result or being transient.

Using the procedure SUM of Example 2 a procedure statement can possibly read

$$SUM\ (i)\ \text{result} : (S[k])$$

and might occur in a loop with k as the controlled variable.

11.3 EXAMPLE

With the help of the procedure *Fourco* declared in Example 9, Section 10.1.4, Fourier coefficients of a function $p(x)$ are to be determined.
Let

$$f(x) = \begin{cases} -x + 0.5 & \text{for} \quad x \leq -1 \\ 2 - 1.5x^2 & \text{for} \quad -1 < x < 1 \\ x/2 & \text{for} \quad x \geq 1 . \end{cases}$$

In addition the sum of squares of the Fourier coefficients

$$s_1 = \sum_{k=0}^{n-1} a_k^2$$

$$s_2 = \sum_{k=0}^{n-1} b_k^2$$

are to be determined by means of the procedure declared in Example 2.

```
            begin integer n;
              read(n);
              begin real l, u, h;
              integer i, z;
              array a, b[0:n];
```

```
              real procedure phi(x);
              value x; real x;
              phi := if abs(x) < 1 then 2 − 1.5 × x × x × x
                else if x ≤ −1 then −x + 0.5 else x/2;
```

```
              procedure SUM(u) result : (RES);
                integer u; real RES;
                begin real s, h;
                  s := 0;
                  i := 1;
            L1:   h := a[u] × a[u];
                  s := s + h;
                  i := i + 1;
                  if u ≤ z then go to L1;
                  RES := s
                end;
```

```
    procedure Fourco(a, b, n, fct, cs) result : (ab);
      value a, b, n;
      real a, b;
      integer n;
      array ab;
      real procedure fct, cs;
      begin integer i, k; real p, q, r, s;
        p := (b − a)/(2 × n);
        q := 6.283185307/(b − a);
        for k := 0 step 1 until n − 1 do
          begin
            r := k × q; s := 0;
            for i := 0 step 1 until 2 × n − 1 do
              s := s + fct(a + i × p) × cs(r × (a + i × p));
            ab[k] := s/n
          end
      end;
```

$read(l, u); print(l, u);$
$z := n - 1;$
$Fourco(l, u, n, phi, cos)$ result : $(a);$
$Fourco(l, u, n, phi, sin)$ result : $(a);$
$SUM(i - 1)$ result : $(h); print(h);$
for $i := 0$ **step** 1 **until** $n - 1$ **do**
    $print(a[i]);$
$SUM(i - 1)$ result : $(h); print(h);$
for $i := 0$ **step** 1 **until** $n - 1$ **do**
        $print(a[i])$
end
end

12 PROCEDURES CALLING THEMSELVES

We have as yet not given an example of a procedure declaration the body of which contains a direct call of the procedure itself, or an indirect regress by means of a procedure called directly in the body of the procedure declaration.

Although it is not simple to give convincing examples of such procedures calling themselves within the domain of numerical analysis which is our primary subject matter we shall try to demonstrate how, in certain situations, the device can be of help notationally.

Suppose that for variable s a certain process should be repeated in s nested loops in the manner indicated as follows:

> **for** $i_s := 1$ **step** 1 **until** n **do**
>> **for** $i_{s-1} := 1$ **step** 1 **until** n **do**

> $\cdot \quad \cdot \quad \cdot$

>> **for** $i_1 := 1$ **step** 1 **until** n **do** $\quad P(i_1, i_2, \ldots, i_s)$

where P represents a given piece of program depending on the variables $i_1, i_2, \ldots, i_s$.

Unfortunately, since even the number of variables i_σ and nested loops is variable, we were forced here to use the "..." notation not formally existing in ALGOL. However, we can get around this difficulty of iterating our basic iteration device, the for clause, by means of a suitable procedure iterating itself.

For setting up the procedure declaration we let ourselves be led by a simple analogy to numerical recursion. A suitable example is summation: We define $s = \sum_{k=1}^{n} a_k$ recursively by

$$s_0 = 0$$
$$s_k = a_k + s_{k-1}$$
$$s = s_n$$

83

By analogy we could define our iterated loop system in the following rather unorthodox way

$$Q_0 \equiv P$$
$$Q_k \equiv \textbf{for } ik := 1 \textbf{ step } 1 \textbf{ until } n \textbf{ do } Q_{k-1}$$
$$Q \equiv Q_s$$

where the use of the identity sign $\equiv$ is intended to show that this is a rule of textual composition and not a rule of computation.

In translating this "literal recursion" into an ALGOL procedure, we replace the set of loop variables by an integer array $i[1:s]$ and assume further that this array, the integer variable s, and the procedure $P(i,s)$ representing our program $P(i1, i2, \ldots, is)$ are properly declared nonlocal quantities.

Our procedure will then have the following form

> **procedure** *loop yourself* (k);
>   **integer** k; **value** k;
>   **if** $k = 0$ **then** $P(i, s)$
>   **else for** $i[k] := 1$ **step** 1 **until** n **do** *loop yourself* $(k - 1)$;

It is clear that the procedure is meaningful only for positive integer values of the argument k since only then the repeated subtraction of 1 leads to a value $k = 0$ terminating the recursion.

In order to see clearly what the procedure does, the reader should work out the complete course of the computation for a small initial value of k, say, $k = 3$. This will show that procedures of this type, although looking deceivingly simple, will, on account of the high number of executions of the procedure call, lead to slow programs burdened by a lot of red tape. This will be tolerable only in the case where execution of a procedure call is negligible compared to a single evaluation of that part of the procedure which describes the real work to be done, in our case the procedure $P(i, s)$.

Examples of this sort seem to be very rare in numerical analysis. In contradistinction, procedures calling themselves are well suited and extensively used for the purposes of symbol manipulation of the kind we used as a guide to construct our example.

Procedures of this type are derived from a notation which was introduced together with conditional expressions, in order to represent in a simple and elegant manner the classical recursive functions of elementary number theory studied extensively in mathematical logic. For this reason procedures calling themselves today are commonly called recursive procedures.

13 EXERCISES

The following set of exercises are grouped according to the chapters of reference, indicated by the first of the two numbers at the left of each exercise.

1.1 Which of the following are numbers according to the ALGOL convention?

(a) -0.31 $+293.995$ $\times 3.5$ $\pm.000005$

(b) (4.55) $3 + 5$ $4 + 5i$ Two

(c) $3.$ 3.0 0030 $.3$

(d) $_{10}5$ $3.5\ 10^9$ $5 \cdot 10^9$ $1.5 \cdot {}_{10}3$

(e) $31.41592_{10} - 1$ $30.30_{10}1.5$ $2_{10}n$ $1_{10}0$

1.2 Which of the following can be used as identifiers?

(a) *arcsin*   *end*   *cos*

(b) $2A$ $\times 2$ *tRACE*

(c) *(name)* $K-25$ $r \times x$

(d) $X2.5$ $One_{10} - 2$ Oo

2.1 Which of the following are valid arithmetic expressions?

(a) $5 \times {}_{10}3$ $5 \times {}_{10}3/2$ $_{10}k$ $5 \times 10 \uparrow 2$ $X \times 52_{10}(i+j)$

(b) $2x + y$ $x - y$ $x \times -y$ $+(-(+(-a)))$ $a \pm b$

(c) $3/x - x$ $nine \times 3$ $x/y/z$ $2/x \times y/2 - z$ $(x - 1)/x - 1$

(d) $y_{10} \uparrow 3$ $x \uparrow + y$ $x \uparrow {}_{10}3$ $3_{10} \uparrow 2$ $_{10}2 \uparrow x$

2.2 The values of the following variables are stipulated to be

$$x1 = 2 \qquad y1 = -2$$
$$x2 = 5 \qquad y2 = 3$$
$$x3 = 1 \qquad y3 = 4$$

Find the value of each of the following expressions

(a) $x1 + y1/2 + y3$
(b) $x1 \uparrow x2 + 3$
(c) $x1 \times (y1 - y3)/(-y2)$
(d) $x1 \uparrow y1 \uparrow y2$
(e) $y2 \uparrow x1 \times y1$
(f) $(y2 + y1) \times x3 - (x1 + y3 \times (x2 - y1))$
(g) $(x1 \uparrow y1) \uparrow y2$
(h) $x1 \uparrow (y1 \uparrow y2)$

2.3 Write the following mathematical expressions in ALGOL form.

(a) $\dfrac{n(n-1)}{2}$ $\qquad \dfrac{a}{b-c}$ $\qquad \dfrac{x-y}{x+\dfrac{x-y}{z}}$

(b) $3x + 2y^2$ $\qquad x + \dfrac{1+x}{x^2}$ $\qquad y + z\dfrac{1+x^2}{x}$

(c) x^{a+b} $\qquad x^{a+b^c}$ $\qquad (x^y)^z$

(d) $\dfrac{1}{\dfrac{1}{a}+\dfrac{1}{b}}$ $\qquad \dfrac{\dfrac{u}{x}}{\dfrac{v}{y}}$ $\qquad \dfrac{x}{y}\left(1+\dfrac{a+b}{v}\right)\dfrac{\dfrac{1}{a}+\dfrac{1}{b}}{c+d}$

2.4 Modify the following expressions suitably using standard functions

(a) $\dfrac{1}{1+x^{1/2}}$ $\qquad$ (b) $t^{3/2}$ $\qquad$ (c) a^{1000}

2.5 State the values printed in the following piece of program.

```
integer i, j;
real x, y, z;
i := 5; j := −2;
x := 3.14; y := i × x/j;
z := x + y × i;
x := y + z;
print(i, j, x, y, z);
```

2.6 State the values printed in the following piece of program.

```
integer a, b, c;
real u, v, w;
a := b := 2;
u := v := 1.2;
w := a + b + u;
c := w + v + a;
print(a, b, c, u, v, w);
```

3.1 The following does not constitute a program; correct it.

```
begin
    real x, y, z
    integer a, b, c
    read(x, y, a, b)
    u := x + y
    z := a × u + c × y
    print x, y, z
end
```

3.2 Why is the following program wrong?

```
begin
    integer a; real b;
    a := b := 2
end
```

3.3 What is the meaning of the following?

$$x := y := y + 1$$

3.4 In a piece of program you find

$$c := cos(t); s := sin(t);$$
$$a := (u \times c + v \times s);$$
$$b := (-u \times s + v \times c);$$

Why is this not written in two statements?

3.5   Write a piece of program to compute

$$\sigma_{rad} = 4\left[\ln\left(2\frac{T + m_0c^2}{m_0c^2}\right) - \frac{1}{3}\right]\sigma_0z^2.$$

4.1   The trapezoid rule is used to approximate

$$I = \int_a^b f(x)\,dx.$$

Briefly, the area under the curve is approximated by the trapezoid area

$$I \approx \frac{b - a}{2}(f(a) + f(b)).$$

A better approximation is obtained when the interval $[a, b]$ is subdivided. In that case I is approximately the sum of the trapezoid areas of the strips. Write a program to approximate the integral of

$$y = \frac{\sin x}{x}$$

from 0 to 1 assuming a subdivision 0, $\frac{1}{3}$, $\frac{2}{3}$, 1.

4.2   Linear interpolation: A function $f(x)$ is said to be linear if

$$f[a, b] = \frac{f(a) - f(b)}{a - b}$$

is constant independently of the values of a and b, $a \neq b$. Hence

$$f[a, b] = f[a, x],$$

from which it follows that

$$f(x) = f(a) + (x - a)f[a, b] = \frac{1}{b - a}[(b - x)f(a) + (x - a)f(b)].$$

Thus,

$$f(x) = \frac{1}{x_2 - x_1}[(x_2 - x_1)f_1 + (x - x_1)f_2]$$

is the linear interpolation function which assumes f_1 for $x = x_1$ and f_2 for $x = x_2$. Assume that in the input medium there are values

$$x_1, f_1, x_2, f_2, x,$$

Write a program that reads in the necessary quantities, computes $f(x)$, and prints the result.

4.3   Write a program to find the value of

$$n_{C_r} = \frac{n(n - 1)(n - 2)\cdots(n - r + 1)}{1\cdot2\cdot3\cdots r}$$

given in the input medium n and r.

4.4   State the value printed in the following program.

```
begin
    real x, y;
    for x := 0 step 0.1 until 0.55 do
        y := (1 − x) ↑ 2;
    print(y)
end
```

What is the value of x when the last statement in the loop is being executed? What is the value of x after the last statement in the loop has been executed?

4.5   Indicate the value printed in the following program.

```
begin
    real x, y;
    integer i;
    x := 0;
    y := 2;
    for i := 1 step 1 until 3 do;
        x := x + 3 × y;
    print(x)
end
```

4.6   Write a piece of program to assign the natural numbers up to 10 to the components of a vector of order 10.

5.1   Newton's method for integral roots:
Let c be an integral root of
$$f(x) = a_n x^n + a_{n-1}x^{n-1} + \cdots + a_1 + a_0$$
where a_i is integral $(i = 0, 1, \ldots, n)$. Then $1/c$ is a root of
$$g(x) = x^n f\left(\frac{1}{x}\right) = a_0 x^n + a_1 x^{n-1} + \cdots + a_n.$$
Using this fact it follows that
$$\left(\cdots\left(\left(\left(a_0 \cdot \frac{1}{c} + a_1\right) \cdot \frac{1}{c} + a_2\right) \cdot \frac{1}{c} + \cdots + a_{n-1}\right) \cdot \frac{1}{c} + a_n = 0.$$

[This is Horner's scheme for evaluating $g(x)$ at $x = 1/c$.] It can therefore be shown that c already fails to be an integral root of $f(x)$ if any of the following partial results of the Horner's scheme fails to be divisible by c.

$$a_0$$

$$a_0 \cdot \frac{1}{c} + a_1$$

$$\left(a_0 \cdot \frac{1}{c} + a_1\right) \cdot \frac{1}{c} + a_2$$

$$\left(\left(a_0 \cdot \frac{1}{c} + a_1\right) \cdot \frac{1}{c} + a_2\right) \cdot \frac{1}{c} + a_3$$

$$\vdots$$

$$\left(\cdots\left(\left(\left(a_0 \cdot \frac{1}{c} + a_1\right) \cdot \frac{1}{c} + a_2\right) \cdot \frac{1}{c} + a_3\right) \cdot \frac{1}{c} + \cdots + a_{n-1}\right.$$

Given n, a_0, a_1, a_2, ..., a_n, c, in the input medium write a program which uses the above-mentioned facts to determine whether c is a zero of $f(x)$ or not. Print 0 if not, 1 if yes.

5.2   All the integral roots of $f(x)$ in Exercise 5.1 can be found by obtaining all the divisors of a_0.

5.3   Newton's method: Given a function $f(x)$ and x_0, an approximation to one of its zeros, a better approximation, x_1, can be obtained (under certain conditions) by

$$x_1 = x_0 - \frac{f(x_0)}{f'(x_0)}.$$

Of course, having found x_1 it may be necessary to find a still better approximation, x_2

$$x_2 = x_1 - \frac{f(x_1)}{f'(x_1)}.$$

In general,

$$x_{i+1} = x_i - \frac{f'(x_i)}{f(x_i)}$$

is a better approximation than x_i. Write a program to approximate the zero of

$$x - \cos x$$

lying between 0 and 1.5 to six significant digits.

5.4   Are the following incorrect?
      If so, why?

(a)

> **real** a, b, c, x, y, z;
> **if** $x < y$ **then if** $x > z$ **then** $a := b$ **else** $a := c$;

(b)

> **integer** i, j, k, l;
> **real** a, b, c, u, v;
>
> $\ldots$
>
> **if** $u < v$ **then**
>   **for** $i := 1$ **step** 1 **until** j **do**
>   **if** $k < l$ **then** $a := b$
>   **else** $a := c$;

6.1   Consider the following statement from a correct program

> **for** $i := 1$ **step** 1 **until** n **do**
>   **begin**
> $a[i] := b[i]$;
>   **goto** $L1$;
> $L2$: $c[i] := d[i]$
>   **end**;

Can the statement labeled $L2$ ever be executed?

7.1 Consider the following:

```
begin
   real x, y, z;
   integer a, b, c;
L1: a := b := c := 1;
   begin
      integer a;
      x := a + 3.141593 × b;


      . . .



   end
end
```

This program is incorrect.

7.2 The following program shows bad programming manners.

```
begin
   real x, y, z;
   integer a, b, c;
L1: a := 1;
   begin
      real u;
      read (x, y, z, b, c);
      go to L1;


      . . .



L1:    u := a × x + z × z + b × y;



      . . .



   end;
```

```
       . . .

    go to L1;


       . . .


    end
```

Change it in order to make its meaning obvious.

7.3   Why is the following wrong?

```
    begin
        integer n,m;
        real x, y, z;
        read(n);
        begin integer n;
            array A[1:n];


            . . .
```

8.1   Write the expressions of Exercise 2.3 without using redundant parentheses.

8.2   Are the following expressions admissible (x, y, z, u, and v are real variables)? If yes, make the meaning obvious by suitable use of parentheses; otherwise, use parentheses to make them meaningful. Can parentheses be used to obtain more than one interpretation?

(a) if $x \le 0$ then u else $v + y$
(b) $x +$ if $y < z$ then u else v
(c) $x +$ if $y < 0$ then u else $v + y$

9.1   Nesting of switches should be handled with care. Consider

```
    switch s := L1, L2, w[2], L3;
    switch w := L4, s[3], L5;
```

9.2   Consider the following

```
begin integer i ;
        real g;


        . . .


        for i := 0 step 1 until 3 do
        begin


            . . .


            go to if g < 0 then i + 1 else p
        end;
    1:  . . .
    2:  . . .
    3:  . . .
    4:  . . .
    p:  . . .
end
```

What is intended with this program? How can it be corrected by a proper switch declaration?

10.1   Indicate the local quantities in the following piece of procedure body.

```
begin integer i, j, k;
    real x, y, z;
    s := n × n + 1;
    i := j := 2;
        for k := 1 step 1 until s do
            x := u + v × v
end
```

10.2 Formal parameters may be called by value only when they are used as arguments. In this case it is to be noted that the corresponding actual parameter is unaltered, an expression is computed once, and the formal parameter is used inside of the procedure. Let x and y be formal parameters in the following procedure body

```
begin
    x := x + 1;
    t := cos((x + y) × 3.14)
end
```

Study the effect of call by value and call by name of x and y. This can be done by considering corresponding actual parameters and noticing their effect when the procedure is executed. For example, let the actual parameters corresponding to x and y be

(a) r, s respectively and assume both having the value 2,
(b) s for both and assume s having the value 2.

Note the difference of the effect of the calls by value and calls by name.

10.3 Look at the following program and insert the proper specifications for A and B.

```
begin
    real t;
    array M[1:10];
    procedure p (A, B); ...A; ...B;
        t := A[5] × B;
        M[5] := 7;
        p(M, M[5]);
        print(t)
end
```

What is the printout?

10.4

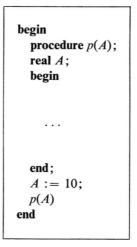

```
begin
    procedure p(A);
    real A;
    begin

        . . .

    end;
    A := 10;
    p(A)
end
```

This program is wrong. Why?

10.5 The innerproduct of two vectors can be written as

$$z = x_1 y_1 + x_2 y_2 + \cdots + x_n y_n.$$

Write a function procedure to do this calculation.

10.6 Let $A = (a_{ik})$ $i = 1, 2, \ldots, n,$ $k = 1, 2, \ldots, m,$
and $B = (b_{ik})$ $i = 1, 2, \ldots, m,$ $k = 1, 2, \ldots, p$
be two rectangular matrices with real elements.

The product

$$C = A \times B$$

is defined by

$$(c_{ik}) = \left(\sum_{j=1}^{m} a_{ij} \times b_{jk} \right) \quad \begin{array}{l} i = 1, 2, \ldots, n \\ k = 1, 2, \ldots, p \end{array}$$

In the corresponding program, there are six different ways of nesting the loops. Write proper procedure declarations.

How can these processes be described in terms of operations on the rows and columns of the matrices involved?

APPENDIX

Revised Report on the Algorithmic Language ALGOL 60*

BY

J. W. BACKUS, F. L. BAUER, J. GREEN, C. KATZ, J. MCCARTHY,
P. NAUR, A. J. PERLIS, H. RUTISHAUSER, K. SAMELSON, B. VAUQUOIS,
J. H. WEGSTEIN, A. VAN WIJNGAARDEN, M. WOODGER

Edited by

PETER NAUR

Dedicated to the memory of WILLIAM TURANSKI

---

* International Federation for Information Processing 1962.

SUMMARY

The report gives a complete defining description of the international algorithmic language ALGOL 60. This is a language suitable for expressing a large class of numerical processes in a form sufficiently concise for direct automatic translation into the language of programmed automatic computers.

The introduction contains an account of the preparatory work leading up to the final conference, where the language was defined. In addition the notions reference language, publication language, and hardware representations are explained.

In the first chapter a survey of the basic constituents and features of the language is given, and the formal notation, by which the syntactic structure is defined, is explained.

The second chapter lists all the basic symbols, and the syntactic units known as identifiers, numbers, and strings are defined. Further some important notions such as quantity and value are defined.

The third chapter explains the rules for forming expressions and the meaning of these expressions. Three different types of expressions exist: arithmetic, Boolean (logical), and designational.

The fourth chapter describes the operational units of the language, known as statements. The basic statements are: assignment statements (evaluation of a formula), go to statements (explicit break of the sequence of execution of statements), dummy statements, and procedure statements (call for execution of a closed process, defined by a procedure declaration). The formation of more complex structures, having statement character, is explained. These include: conditional statements, for statements, compound statements, and blocks.

In the fifth chapter the units known as declarations, serving for defining permanent properties of the units entering into a process described in the language, are defined.

The report ends with two detailed examples of the use of the language and an alphabetic index of definitions.

INTRODUCTION

BACKGROUND

After the publication [1,2] of a preliminary report on the algorithmic language ALGOL, as prepared at a conference in Zürich in 1958, much interest in the ALGOL language developed.

As a result of an informal meeting held at Mainz in November 1958, about forty interested persons from several European countries held an ALGOL implementation conference in Copenhagen in February 1959. A "hardware group" was formed for working cooperatively right down to the level of the paper tape code. This conference also led to the publication by Regnecentralen, Copenhagen, of an *Algol Bulletin*, edited by PETER NAUR, which served as a forum for further discussion. During the June 1959 ICIP Conference in Paris several meetings, both formal and informal ones, were held. These meetings revealed some misunderstandings as to the intent of the group which was primarily responsible for the formulation of the language, but at the same time made it clear that there exists a wide appreciation of the effort involved. As a result of the discussions it was decided to hold an international meeting in January 1960 for improving the ALGOL language and preparing a final report. At a European ALGOL Conference in Paris in November 1959 which was attended by about fifty people, seven European representatives were selected to attend the January 1960 Conference, and they represent the following organizations: Association Française de Calcul, British Computer Society, Gesellschaft für Angewandte Mathematik und Mechanik, and Nederlands Rekenmachine Genootschap. The seven representatives held a final preparatory meeting at Mainz in December 1959.

Meanwhile, in the United States, anyone who wished to suggest changes or corrections to ALGOL was requested to send his comments to the *Communications of the ACM*, where they were published. These comments then became the basis of consideration for changes in the ALGOL language. Both the SHARE and USE organizations established ALGOL working groups, and both organizations were represented on the ACM Committee on Program-

---

[1] Preliminary report—International Algebraic Language, Comm. Assoc. Comp. Mach. 1, No. 12 (1958), 8.

[2] Report on the Algorithmic Language ALGOL by the ACM Committee on Programming Languages and the GAMM Committee on Programming, edited by A. J. PERLIS and K. SAMELSON, *Numerische Mathematik* Bd. 1, S. 41–60 (1959).

ming Languages. The ACM Committee met in Washington in November 1959 and considered all comments on ALGOL that had been sent to the ACM *Communications*. Also, seven representatives were selected to attend the January 1960 international conference. These seven representatives held a final preparatory meeting in Boston in December 1959.

JANUARY 1960 CONFERENCE

The thirteen representatives,[3] from Denmark, England, France, Germany, Holland, Switzerland, and the United States, conferred in Paris from January 11 to 16, 1960.

Prior to this meeting a completely new draft report was worked out from the preliminary report and the recommendations of the preparatory meetings by PETER NAUR and the Conference adopted this new form as the basis for its report. The Conference then proceeded to work for agreement on each item of the report. The present report represents the union of the Committee's concepts and the intersection of its agreements.

APRIL 1962 CONFERENCE [EDITED BY M. WOODGER]

A meeting of some of the authors of ALGOL 60 was held on 2nd–3rd April 1962 in Rome, Italy, through the facilities and courtesy of the International Computation Centre. The following were present:

Authors	*Advisers*	*Observer*
F. L. BAUER	M. PAUL	W. L. VAN DER POEL
J. GREEN	R. FRANCIOTTI	(Chairman, IFIP TC 2.1
C. KATZ	P. Z. INGERMAN	Working Group ALGOL)
R. KOGON (representing		
J. W. BACKUS)		
P. NAUR		
K. SAMELSON	G. SEEGMÜLLER	
J. H. WEGSTEIN	R. E. UTMAN	
A. VAN WIJNGAARDEN		
M. WOODGER	P. LANDIN	

The purpose of the meeting was to correct known errors in, attempt to eliminate apparent ambiguities in, and otherwise clarify the ALGOL 60 Report. Extensions to the language were not considered at the meeting. Various proposals for correction and clarification that were submitted by interested parties in response to the Questionnaire in *Algol Bulletin* No. 14 were used as a guide.

---

[3] WILLIAM TURANSKI of the American group was killed by an automobile just prior to the January 1960 Conference.

This report[1] constitutes a supplement to the ALGOL 60 Report which should resolve a number of difficulties therein. Not all of the questions raised concerning the original report could be resolved. Rather than risk hastily drawn conclusions on a number of subtle points, which might create new ambiguities, the committee decided to report only those points which they unanimously felt could be stated in clear and unambiguous fashion.

Questions concerned with the following areas are left for further consideration by Working Group 2.1 of IFIP, in the expectation that current work on advanced programming languages will lead to better resolution:

1. Side effects of functions.
2. The call by name concept.
3. **own**: static or dynamic.
4. For statement: static or dynamic.
5. Conflict between specification and declaration.

The authors of the ALGOL 60 Report present at the Rome Conference, being aware of the formation of a Working Group on ALGOL by IFIP, accepted that any collective responsibility which they might have with respect to the development, specification, and refinement of the ALGOL language will from now on be transferred to that body.

This report has been reviewed by IFIP TC 2 on Programming Languages in August 1962 and has been approved by the Council of the International Federation for Information Processing.

As with the preliminary ALGOL report, three different levels of language are recognized, namely a Reference Language, a Publication Language, and several Hardware Representations.

Reference Language

1. It is the working language of the committee.
2. It is the defining language.
3. The characters are determined by ease of mutual understanding and not by any computer limitations, coders notation, or pure mathematical notation.
4. It is the basic reference and guide for compiler builders.
5. It is the guide for all hardware representations.
6. It is the guide for transliterating from publication language to any locally appropriate hardware representations.

---

[1] [Editor's note: The present edition follows the text which was approved by the Council of IFIP. Although it is not clear from the Introduction, the present version is the original report of the January 1960 conference modified according to the agreements reached during the April 1962 conference. Thus the report mentioned here is incorporated in the present version. The modifications touch the original report in the following sections: Changes of text: 1 with footnote; 2.1 footnote; 2.3; 2.7; 3.3.3; 3.3.4.2; 4.1.3; 4.2.3; 4.2.4; 4.3.4; 4.7.3; 4.7.3.1; 4.7.3.3; 4.7.5.1; 4.7.5.4; 4.7.6; 5; 5.3.3; 5.3.5; 5.4.3; 5.4.4; 5.4.5. Changes of syntax: 3.4.1; 4.1.1; 4.2.1; 4.5.1.]

7. The main publications of the ALGOL language itself will use the reference representation.

Publication Language

1. The publication language admits variations of the reference language according to usage of printing and handwriting (e.g., subscripts, spaces, exponents, Greek letters).

2. It is used for stating and communicating processes.

3. The characters to be used may be different in different countries, but univocal correspondence with reference representation must be secured.

Hardware Representations

1. Each one of these is a condensation of the reference language enforced by the limited number of characters on standard input equipment.

2. Each one of these uses the character set of a particular computer and is the language accepted by a translator for that computer.

3. Each one of these must be accompanied by a special set of rules for transliterating from publication or reference language.

For transliteration between the reference language and a language suitable for publications, among others, the following rules are recommended.

Reference language	Publication language
Subscript brackets [ ]	Lowering of the line between the brackets and removal of the brackets.
Exponentiation $\uparrow$	Raising of the exponent.
Parentheses ( )	Any form of parentheses, brackets, braces.
Basis of ten $_{10}$	Raising of the ten and of the following integral number, inserting of the intended multiplication sign.

Description of the Reference Language

Was sich überhaupt sagen läßt, läßt sich
klar sagen; und wovon man nicht reden
kann, darüber muß man schweigen.
LUDWIG WITTGENSTEIN

I. STRUCTURE OF THE LANGUAGE

As stated in the introduction, the algorithmic language has three different kinds of representations—reference, hardware, and publication—and the development described in the sequel is in terms of the reference representation. This means that all objects defined within the language are represented by a given set of symbols—and it is only in the choice of symbols that the other two representations may differ. Structure and content must be the same for all representations.

The purpose of the algorithmic language is to describe computational processes. The basic concept used for the description of calculating rules is the well known arithmetic expression containing as constituents numbers, variables, and functions. From such expressions are compounded, by applying rules of arithmetic composition, self-contained units of the language—explicit formulae—called assignment statements.

To show the flow of computational processes, certain nonarithmetic statements and statement clauses are added which may describe, e.g., alternatives, or iterative repetitions of computing statements. Since it is necessary for the function of these statements that one statement refers to another, statements may be provided with labels. A sequence of statements may be enclosed between the statement brackets **begin** and **end** to form a compound statement.

Statements are supported by declarations which are not themselves computing instructions, but inform the translator of the existence and certain properties of objects appearing in statements, such as the class of numbers taken on as values by a variable, the dimension of an array of numbers, or even the set of rules defining a function. A sequence of declarations followed by a sequence of statements and enclosed between **begin** and **end** constitutes a block. Every declaration appears in a block in this way and is valid only for that block.

A program is a block or compound statement which is not contained within another statement and which makes no use of other statements not contained within it.

In the sequel the syntax and semantics of the language will be given. [1]

1.1. FORMALISM FOR SYNTACTIC DESCRIPTION

The syntax will be described with the aid of metalinguistic formulae. [2] Their interpretation is best explained by an example:

⟨ab⟩ ::= (| [| ⟨ab⟩(| ⟨ab⟩⟨d⟩

Sequences of characters enclosed in the bracket ⟨ ⟩ represent metalinguistic variables whose values are sequences of symbols. The marks ::= and | (the latter with the meaning of **or**) are metalinguistic connectives. Any mark in a formula, which is not a variable or a connective, denotes itself (or the class of marks which are similar to it). Juxtaposition of marks and/or variables in a formula signifies juxtaposition of the sequences denoted. Thus the formula above gives a recursive rule for the formation of values of the variable ⟨ab⟩. It indicates that ⟨ab⟩ may have the value (or [or that given some legitimate value of ⟨ab⟩, another may be formed by following it with the character (or by following it with some value of the variable ⟨d⟩. If the values of ⟨d⟩ are the decimal digits, some values of ⟨ab⟩ are:

[((((1(37(
(12345(
(((
[86

In order to facilitate the study, the symbols used for distinguishing the meta-linguistic variables (i.e., the sequences of characters appearing within the brackets ⟨ ⟩ as ab in the above example) have been chosen to be words describing approximately the nature of the corresponding variable. Where words which have appeared in this manner are used elsewhere in the text they will refer to the corresponding syntactic definition. In addition some formulae have been given in more than one place.

DEFINITION:

⟨empty⟩ ::=

(i.e., the null string of symbols).

---

[1] Whenever the precision of arithmetic is stated as being in general not specified, or the outcome of a certain process is left undefined or said to be undefined, this is to be interpreted in the sense that a program only fully defines a computational process if the accompanying information specifies the precision assumed, the kind of arithmetic assumed, and the course of action to be taken in all such cases as may occur during the execution of the computation.

[2] Cf. J. W. BACKUS, The syntax and semantics of the proposed international algebraic language of the Zürich ACM-GAMM conference. ICIP Paris, June 1959.

2. BASIC SYMBOLS, IDENTIFIERS, NUMBERS, AND STRINGS. BASIC CONCEPTS

The reference language is built up from the following basic symbols:

⟨basic symbol⟩ ::= ⟨letter⟩ | ⟨digit⟩ | ⟨logical value⟩ | ⟨delimiter⟩

2.1. LETTERS

$$\langle \text{letter} \rangle ::= a|b|c|d|e|f|g|h|i|j|k|l|m|n|o|p|q|r|s|t|u|v|w|x|y|z|$$
$$A|B|C|D|E|F|G|H|I|J|K|L|M|N|O|P|Q|R|S|T|U|V|W|X|Y|Z$$

This alphabet may arbitrarily be restricted, or extended with any other distinctive character (i.e., character not coinciding with any digit, logical value, or delimiter).

Letters do not have individual meaning. They are used for forming identifiers and strings[1] (cf. Sections 2.4. Identifiers, 2.6. Strings).

2.2.1. DIGITS

⟨digit⟩ ::= 0|1|2|3|4|5|6|7|8|9

Digits are used for forming numbers, identifiers, and strings.

2.2.2. LOGICAL VALUES

⟨logical value⟩ ::= **true**|**false**

The logical values have a fixed obvious meaning.

2.3. DELIMITERS

⟨delimiter⟩ ::= ⟨operator⟩ | ⟨separator⟩ | ⟨bracket⟩ | ⟨declarator⟩ |
    ⟨specificator⟩
⟨operator⟩ ::= ⟨arithmetic operator⟩ | ⟨relational operator⟩ |
    ⟨logical operator⟩ | ⟨sequential operator⟩
⟨arithmetic operator⟩ ::= + | − | × | / | ÷ | ↑
⟨relational operator⟩ ::= < | ≤ | = | ≥ | > | ≠
⟨logical operator⟩ ::= ≡ | ⊃ | ∨ | ∧ | ¬
⟨sequential operator⟩ ::= **go to** | **if** | **then** | **else** | **for** | **do**[2]
⟨separator⟩ ::= , | . | $_{10}$ | : | ; | := | ⊔ | **step** | **until** | **while** | **comment**

---

[1] It should be particularly noted that throughout the reference language underlining [in typewritten copy; boldface type in printed copy—Ed.] is used for defining independent basic symbols (see sections 2.2.2 and 2.3). These are understood to have no relation to the individual letters of which they are composed. Within the present report [not including headings—Ed.] underlining [boldface—Ed.] will be used for no other purposes.

[2] **do** is used in for statements. It has no relation whatsoever to the *do* of the preliminary report, which is not included in ALGOL 60.

⟨bracket⟩ ::= (|) | [|] | ' | ' | **begin** | **end**
⟨declarator⟩ ::= **own** | **Boolean** | **integer** | **real** | **array** | **switch** | **procedure**
⟨specificator⟩ ::= **string** | **label** | **value**

Delimiters have a fixed meaning which for the most part is obvious or else will be given at the appropriate place in the sequel.

Typographical features such as blank space or change to a new line have no significance in the reference language. They may, however, be used freely for facilitating reading.

For the purpose of including text among the symbols of a program the following "comment" conventions hold:

The sequence of basic symbols:	is equivalent to
; **comment** ⟨any sequence not containing ;⟩;	;
begin comment ⟨any sequence not containing ;⟩;	**begin**
end ⟨any sequence not containing **end** or ; or **else**⟩	**end**

By equivalence is here meant that any of the three structures shown in the left hand column may be replaced, in any occurrence outside of strings, by the symbol shown on the same line in the right hand column without any effect on the action of the program. It is further understood that the comment structure encountered first in the text when reading from left to right has precedence in being replaced over later structures contained in the sequence.

2.4. IDENTIFIERS

2.4.1. SYNTAX

⟨identifier⟩ ::= ⟨letter⟩ | ⟨identifier⟩⟨letter⟩ | ⟨identifier⟩⟨digit⟩

2.4.2. EXAMPLES

$$q$$
$$Soup$$
$$V17a$$
$$a34kTMNs$$
$$MARILYN$$

2.4.3. SEMANTICS

Identifiers have no inherent meaning, but serve for the identification of simple variables, arrays, labels, switches, and procedures. They may be chosen freely (cf. however, Section 3.2.4. Standard functions).

The same identifier cannot be used to denote two different quantities except when these quantities have disjoint scopes as defined by the declarations of the program (cf. Section 2.7. Quantities, kinds and scopes and Section 5. Declarations).

2.5. NUMBERS

2.5.1. SYNTAX

⟨unsigned integer⟩ ::= ⟨digit⟩ | ⟨unsigned integer⟩⟨digit⟩
⟨integer⟩ ::= ⟨unsigned integer⟩ | +⟨unsigned integer⟩ | −⟨unsigned integer⟩

⟨decimal fraction⟩ ::=. ⟨unsigned integer⟩
⟨exponent part⟩ ::=$_{10}$ ⟨integer⟩
⟨decimal number⟩ ::= ⟨unsigned integer⟩ | ⟨decimal fraction⟩ |
    ⟨unsigned integer⟩⟨decimal fraction⟩
⟨unsigned number⟩ ::= ⟨decimal number⟩ | ⟨exponent part⟩ |
    ⟨decimal number⟩⟨exponent part⟩
⟨number⟩ ::= ⟨unsigned number⟩| + ⟨unsigned number⟩ |
    − ⟨unsigned number⟩

2.5.2. EXAMPLES

0	*− 200.084*	*−.083$_{10}$− 02*
177	*+ 07.43$_{10}$8*	*−$_{10}$7*
.5384	*9.34$_{10}$+ 10*	*$_{10}$− 4*
+0.7300	*2$_{10}$− 4*	*+$_{10}$+ 5*

2.5.3. SEMANTICS

Decimal numbers have their conventional meaning. The exponent part is a scale factor expressed as an integral power of 10.

2.5.4. TYPES

Integers are of type **integer**. All other numbers are of type **real** (cf. Section 5.1. Type declarations).

2.6. STRINGS

2.6.1. SYNTAX

⟨proper string⟩ ::= ⟨any sequence of basic symbols not containing ' or '⟩ |
    ⟨empty⟩
⟨open string⟩ ::= ⟨proper string⟩ | ' ⟨open string⟩ ' |
    ⟨open string⟩⟨open string⟩
⟨string⟩ ::= ' ⟨open string⟩ '

2.6.2. EXAMPLES

$$'5k,,-'[[['\wedge=/:'Tt''$$
$$'..This_{⊔}is_{⊔}a_{⊔}' string' '$$

2.6.3. SEMANTICS

In order to enable the language to handle arbitrary sequences of basic symbols the string quotes ' and ' are introduced. The symbol $_{⊔}$ denotes a space. It has no significance outside strings.

Strings are used as actual parameters of procedures (cf. Sections 3.2. Function designators and 4.7. Procedure statements).

2.7. QUANTITIES, KINDS AND SCOPES

The following kinds of quantities are distinguished: simple variables, arrays, labels, switches, and procedures.

The scope of a quantity is the set of statements and expressions in which the declaration of the identifier associated with that quantity is valid. For labels see Section 4.1.3.

2.8. VALUES AND TYPES

A value is an ordered set of numbers (special case: a single number), an ordered set of logical values (special case: a single logical value), or a label.

Certain of the syntactic units are said to possess values. These values will in general change during the execution of the program. The values of expressions and their constituents are defined in Section 3. The value of an array identifier is the ordered set of values of the corresponding array of subscripted variables (cf. Section 3.1.4.1).

The various "types" (**integer**, **real**, **Boolean**) basically denote properties of values. The types associated with syntactic units refer to the values of these units.

3. EXPRESSIONS

In the language the primary constituents of the programs describing algorithmic processes are arithmetic, Boolean, and designational expressions. Constituents of these expressions, except for certain delimiters, are logical values, numbers, variables, function designators, and elementary arithmetic, relational, logical, and sequential operators. Since the syntactic definition of both variables and function designators contains expressions, the definition of expressions, and their constituents, is necessarily recursive.

⟨expression⟩ ::= ⟨arithmetic expression⟩ | ⟨Boolean expression⟩ |
   ⟨designational expression⟩

3.1. VARIABLES

3.1.1. SYNTAX
⟨variable identifier⟩ ::= ⟨identifier⟩
⟨simple variable⟩ ::= ⟨variable identifier⟩
⟨subscript expression⟩ ::= ⟨arithmetic expression⟩
⟨subscript list⟩ ::= ⟨subscript expression⟩ |
   ⟨subscript list⟩, ⟨subscript expression⟩
⟨array identifier⟩ ::= ⟨identifier⟩
⟨subscripted variable⟩ ::= ⟨array identifier⟩ [⟨subscript list⟩]
⟨variable⟩ ::= ⟨simple variable⟩ | ⟨subscripted variable⟩

3.1.2. EXAMPLES

epsilon
det A
a17
Q[7, 2]
x[sin (n × pi/2), Q[3, n, 4]]

3.1.3. SEMANTICS

A variable is a designation given to a single value. This value may be used in expressions for forming other values and may be changed at will by means of assignment statements (Section 4.2). The type of the value of a particular variable is defined in the declaration for the variable itself (cf. Section 5.1. Type declarations) or for the corresponding array identifier (cf. Section 5.2. Array declarations).

3.1.4. SUBSCRIPTS

3.1.4.1. Subscripted variables designate values which are components of multidimensional arrays (cf. Section 5.2. Array declarations). Each arithmetic expression of the subscript list occupies one subscript position of the sub-scripted variable and is called a subscript. The complete list of subscripts is enclosed in the subscript brackets [ ]. The array component referred to by a subscripted variable is specified by the actual numerical value of its subscripts (cf. Section 3.3. Arithmetic expressions).

3.1.4.2. Each subscript position acts like a variable of type **integer** and the evaluation of the subscript is understood to be equivalent to an assignment to this fictitious variable (cf. Section 4.2.4). The value of the subscripted variable is defined only if the value of the subscript expression is within the subscript bounds of the array (cf. Section 5.2. Array declarations).

3.2. FUNCTION DESIGNATORS

3.2.1. SYNTAX

⟨procedure identifier⟩ ∷= ⟨identifier⟩
⟨actual parameter⟩ ∷= ⟨string⟩ | ⟨expression⟩ | ⟨array identifier⟩ |
    ⟨switch identifier⟩ | ⟨procedure identifier⟩
⟨letter string⟩ ∷= ⟨letter⟩ | ⟨letter string⟩⟨letter⟩
⟨parameter delimiter⟩ ∷=, |) ⟨letter string⟩ :(
⟨actual parameter list⟩ ∷= ⟨actual parameter⟩ |
    ⟨actual parameter list⟩⟨parameter delimiter⟩⟨actual parameter⟩
⟨actual parameter part⟩ ∷= ⟨empty⟩ | (⟨actual parameter list⟩)
⟨function designator⟩ ∷= ⟨procedure identifier⟩⟨actual parameter part⟩

3.2.2. EXAMPLES

$$sin\,(a - b)$$
$$J(v + s, n)$$
$$R$$
$$S(s - 5)\ Temperature:\ (T)\ Pressure:\ (P)$$
$$Compile\ (':=')\ Stack:\ (Q)$$

3.2.3. SEMANTICS

Function designators define single numerical or logical values which result through the application of given sets of rules defined by a procedure declaration (cf. Section 5.4. Procedure declarations) to fixed sets of actual parameters.

The rules governing specification of actual parameters are given in Section 4.7. Procedure statements. Not every procedure declaration defines the value of a function designator.

3.2.4. Standard functions

Certain identifiers should be reserved for the standard functions of analysis, which will be expressed as procedures. It is recommended that this reserved list should contain:

abs (E)   for the modulus (absolute value) of the value of the expression E
sign (E)   for the sign of the value of E($+1$ for E > 0, 0 for E $= 0$, -1 for E < 0)
sqrt (E)   for the square root of the value of E
sin (E)   for the sine of the value of E
cos (E)   for the cosine of the value of E
arctan (E) for the principal value of the arctangent of the value of E
ln (E)   for the natural logarithm of the value of E
exp (E)   for the exponential function of the value of E (e^E)

These functions are all understood to operate indifferently on arguments both of type **real** and **integer**. They will all yield values of type **real**, except for *sign* (E) which will have values of type **integer**. In a particular representation these functions may be available without explicit declarations (cf. Section 5. Declarations).

3.2.5. Transfer functions

It is understood that transfer functions between any pair of quantities and expressions may be defined. Among the standard functions it is recommended that there be one, namely

$$entier \text{ (E)},$$

which "transfers" an expression of real type to one of integer type, and assigns to it the value which is the largest integer not greater than the value of E.

3.3. ARITHMETIC EXPRESSIONS

3.3.1. Syntax

⟨adding operator⟩ ::= $+$ | $-$
⟨multiplying operator⟩ ::= $\times$ | / | $\div$
⟨primary⟩ ::= ⟨unsigned number⟩ | ⟨variable⟩ | ⟨function designator⟩ | (⟨arithmetic expression⟩)
⟨factor⟩ ::= ⟨primary⟩ | ⟨factor⟩ ↑ ⟨primary⟩
⟨term⟩ ::= ⟨factor⟩ | ⟨term⟩⟨multiplying operator⟩⟨factor⟩
⟨simple arithmetic expression⟩ ::= ⟨term⟩ | ⟨adding operator⟩⟨term⟩ | ⟨simple arithmetic expression⟩⟨adding operator⟩⟨term⟩

⟨if clause⟩ ::= **if** ⟨Boolean expression⟩ **then**
⟨arithmetic expression⟩ ::= ⟨simple arithmetic expression⟩ |
    ⟨if clause⟩⟨simple arithmetic expression⟩ **else** ⟨arithmetic expression⟩

3.3.2. EXAMPLES

Primaries:

$7.394_{10} - 8$

sum

$w[i + 2, 8]$

$cos(y + z \times 3)$

$(a - 3/y + vu \uparrow 8)$

Factors:

omega

$sum \uparrow cos(y + z \times 3)$

$7.394_{10} - 8 \uparrow w[i + 2, 8] \uparrow (a - 3/y + vu \uparrow 8)$

Terms:

U

$omega \times sum \uparrow cos(y + z \times 3)/7.394_{10} - 8 \uparrow w[i + 2, 8] \uparrow (a - 3/y + vu \uparrow 8)$

Simple arithmetic expression:

$U - Yu + omega \times sum \uparrow cos(y + z \times 3)/7.394_{10} - 8 \uparrow w[i+2,8] \uparrow (a-3/y+vu \uparrow 8)$

Arithmetic expressions:

$w \times u - Q(S + Cu) \uparrow 2$

if $q > 0$ **then** $S + 3 \times Q/A$ **else** $2 \times S + 3 \times q$

if $a < 0$ **then** $U + V$ **else if** $a \times b > 17$ **then** U/V **else if** $k \neq y$ **then** V/U **else** 0

$a \times sin(omega \times t)$

$0.57_{10}12 \times a[N \times (N - 1)/2, 0]$

$(A \times arctan(y) + Z) \uparrow (7 + Q)$

if q **then** $n - 1$ **else** n

if $a < 0$ **then** A/B **else if** $b = 0$ **then** B/A **else** z

3.3.3. SEMANTICS

An arithmetic expression is a rule for computing a numerical value. In case of simple arithmetic expressions this value is obtained by executing the indicated arithmetic operations on the actual numerical values of the primaries of the expression, as explained in detail in Section 3.3.4 below. The actual numerical value of a primary is obvious in the case of numbers. For variables it is the current value (assigned last in the dynamic sense), and for function designators it is the value arising from the computing rules defining the procedure (cf. Section 5.4.4. Values of function designators) when applied to the current values of the procedure parameters given in the expression.

Finally, for arithmetic expressions enclosed in parentheses the value must through a recursive analysis be expressed in terms of the values of primaries of the other three kinds.

In the more general arithmetic expressions, which include if clauses, one out of several simple arithmetic expressions is selected on the basis of the actual values of the Boolean expressions (cf. Section 3.4. Boolean expressions). This selection is made as follows: The Boolean expressions of the if clauses are evaluated one by one in sequence from left to right until one having the value **true** is found. The value of the arithmetic expression is then the value of the first arithmetic expression following this Boolean (the largest arithmetic expression found in this position is understood). The construction:

    else ⟨simple arithmetic expression⟩

is equivalent to the construction:

    else if true then ⟨simple arithmetic expression⟩

3.3.4. OPERATORS AND TYPES

Apart from the Boolean expressions of if clauses, the constituents of simple arithmetic expressions must be of types **real** or **integer** (cf. Section 5.1. Type declarations). The meaning of the basic operators and the types of the expressions to which they lead are given by the following rules:

3.3.4.1. The operators $+$, $-$, and $\times$ have the conventional meaning (addition, subtraction, and multiplication). The type of the expression will be **integer** if both of the operands are of **integer** type, otherwise **real**.

3.3.4.2. The operations ⟨term⟩/⟨factor⟩ and ⟨term⟩ $\div$ ⟨factor⟩ both denote division, to be understood as a multiplication of the term by the reciprocal of the factor with due regard to the rules of precedence (cf. Section 3.3.5). Thus for example

    $a/b \times 7/(p - q) \times v/s$

means

    $((((a \times (b^{-1})) \times 7) \times ((p - q)^{-1})) \times v) \times (s^{-1})$

The operator $/$ is defined for all four combinations of types **real** and **integer** and will yield results of **real** type in any case. The operator $\div$ is defined only for two operands both of type **integer** and will yield a result of type **integer**, mathematically defined as follows:

    $a \div b = sign\,(a/b) \times entier\,(abs\,(a/b))$

(cf. Sections 3.2.4 and 3.2.5).

3.3.4.3. The operation ⟨factor⟩ $\uparrow$ ⟨primary⟩ denotes exponentiation, where the factor is the base and the primary is the exponent. Thus for example

    $2 \uparrow n \uparrow k$ means $(2^n)^k$

while

    $2 \uparrow (n \uparrow m)$ means $2^{(n^m)}$

Writing i for a number of **integer** type, r for a number of **real** type, and a for a number of either **integer** or **real** type, the result is given by the following rules:

$a \uparrow i$ If $i > 0$: $a \times a \times \cdots \times a$ (i times), of the same type as a.

           If $i = 0$,   if $a \neq 0$: 1, of the same type as a.

                    if $a = 0$:   undefined.

           If $i < 0$,   if $a \neq 0$: $1/(a \times a \times \cdots \times a)$ (the denominator has $-i$ factors), of type **real**.

                    if $a = 0$:   undefined.

$a \uparrow r$ If $a > 0$: $exp\,(r \times ln\,(a))$, of type **real**.

           If $a = 0$,   if $r > 0$: 0.0, of type **real**.

                    if $r \leq 0$:   undefined.

           If $a < 0$:   always undefined.

3.3.5. PRECEDENCE OF OPERATORS

The sequence of operations within one expression is generally from left to right, with the following additional rules:

3.3.5.1. According to the syntax given in Section 3.3.1 the following rules of precedence hold:

first: $\uparrow$

second: $\times\,/\div$

third: $+\,-$

3.3.5.2. The expression between a left parenthesis and the matching right parenthesis is evaluated by itself and this value is used in subsequent calculations. Consequently the desired order of execution of operations within an expression can always be arranged by appropriate positioning of parentheses.

3.3.6. ARITHMETICS OF **real** QUANTITIES

Numbers and variables of type **real** must be interpreted in the sense of numerical analysis, i.e., as entities defined inherently with only a finite accuracy. Similarly, the possibility of the occurrence of a finite deviation from the mathematically defined result in any arithmetic expression is explicitly understood. No exact arithmetic will be specified, however, and it is indeed understood that different hardware representations may evaluate arithmetic expressions differently. The control of the possible consequences of such differences must be carried out by the methods of numerical analysis. This control must be considered a part of the process to be described, and will therefore be expressed in terms of the language itself.

3.4. BOOLEAN EXPRESSIONS

3.4.1. SYNTAX

$\langle$relational operator$\rangle ::= \,< \,|\, \leq \,|\, = \,|\, \geq \,|\, > \,|\, \neq$

⟨relation⟩ ::= ⟨simple arithmetic expression⟩⟨relational operator⟩
    ⟨simple arithmetic expression⟩
⟨Boolean primary⟩ ::= ⟨logical value⟩ | ⟨variable⟩ | ⟨function designator⟩ |
    ⟨relation⟩ | (⟨Boolean expression⟩)
⟨Boolean secondary⟩ ::= ⟨Boolean primary⟩ | ¬⟨Boolean primary⟩
⟨Boolean factor⟩ ::= ⟨Boolean secondary⟩ |
    ⟨Boolean factor⟩ ∧ ⟨Boolean secondary⟩
⟨Boolean term⟩ ::= ⟨Boolean factor⟩ | ⟨Boolean term⟩ ∨ ⟨Boolean factor⟩
⟨implication⟩ ::= ⟨Boolean term⟩ | ⟨implication⟩ ⊃ ⟨Boolean term⟩
⟨simple Boolean⟩ ::= ⟨implication⟩ | ⟨simple Boolean⟩ ≡ ⟨implication⟩
⟨Boolean expression⟩ ::= ⟨simple Boolean⟩ |
    ⟨if clause⟩⟨simple Boolean⟩ **else** ⟨Boolean expression⟩

3.4.2. EXAMPLES

$$x = -2$$
$$Y > V \lor z < q$$
$$a + b > -5 \land z - d > q \uparrow 2$$
$$p \land q \lor x \neq y$$
$$g \equiv \neg a \land b \land \neg c \lor d \lor e \supset \neg f$$
if $k < 1$ **then** $s > w$ **else** $h \leq c$
if if if a **then** b **else** c **then** d **else** f **then** g **else** $h < k$

3.4.3. SEMANTICS

A Boolean expression is a rule for computing a logical value. The principles of evaluation are entirely analogous to those given for arithmetic expressions in Section 3.3.3.

3.4.4. TYPES

Variables and function designators entered as Boolean primaries must be declared **Boolean** (cf. Section 5.1. Type declarations and Section 5.4.4. Values of function designators).

3.4.5. THE OPERATORS

Relations take on the value **true** whenever the corresponding relation is satisfied for the expressions involved, otherwise **false**.

The meaning of the logical operators ¬ (not), ∧ (and), ∨ (or), ⊃ (implies), and ≡ (equivalent), is given by the following function table.

$b1$	false	false	true	true
$b2$	false	true	false	true
$\neg b1$	true	true	false	false
$b1 \land b2$	false	false	false	true
$b1 \lor b2$	false	true	true	true
$b1 \supset b2$	true	true	false	true
$b1 \equiv b2$	true	false	false	true

3.4.6. Precedence of operators

The sequence of operations within one expression is generally from left to right, with the following additional rules:

3.4.6.1. According to the syntax given in Section 3.4.1 the following rules of precedence hold:

first: arithmetic expressions according to Section 3.3.5.
second: $< \leqq = \geqq > \neq$
third: $\neg$
fourth: $\wedge$
fifth: $\vee$
sixth: $\supset$
seventh: $\equiv$

3.4.6.2. The use of parentheses will be interpreted in the sense given in Section 3.3.5.2.

3.5. DESIGNATIONAL EXPRESSIONS

3.5.1. Syntax

⟨label⟩ ::= ⟨identifier⟩ | ⟨unsigned integer⟩
⟨switch identifier⟩ ::= ⟨identifier⟩
⟨switch designator⟩ ::= ⟨switch identifier⟩[⟨subscript expression⟩]
⟨simple designational expression⟩ ::= ⟨label⟩ | ⟨switch designator⟩ |
　(⟨designational expression⟩)
⟨designational expression⟩ ::= ⟨simple designational expression⟩ |
　⟨if clause⟩⟨simple designational expression⟩ **else** ⟨designational expression⟩

3.5.2. Examples

17
p9
Choose [*n* − *1*]
Town [**if** *y* < *0* **then** *N* **else** *N* + *1*]
if *Ab* < *c* **then** *17* **else** *q* [**if** *w* ≦ *0* **then** *2* **else** *n*]

3.5.3. Semantics

A designational expression is a rule for obtaining a label of a statement (cf. Section 4. Statements). Again the principle of the evaluation is entirely analogous to that of arithmetic expressions (Section 3.3.3). In the general case the Boolean expressions of the if clauses will select a simple designational expression. If this is a label the desired result is already found. A switch designator refers to the corresponding switch declaration (cf. Section 5.3. Switch declarations) and by the actual numerical value of its subscript expression selects one of the designational expressions listed in the switch declaration by counting these from left to right. Since the designational expression thus selected may again be a switch designator this evaluation is obviously a recursive process.

3.5.4. THE SUBSCRIPT EXPRESSION

The evaluation of the subscript expression is analogous to that of sub-scripted variables (cf. Section 3.1.4.2). The value of a switch designator is defined only if the subscript expression assumes one of the positive values $1, 2, 3, \ldots, n$, where n is the number of entries in the switch list.

3.5.5. UNSIGNED INTEGERS AS LABELS

Unsigned integers used as labels have the property that leading zeroes do not affect their meaning, e.g., *00217* denotes the same label as *217*.

4. STATEMENTS

The units of operation within the language are called statements. They will normally be executed consecutively as written. However, this sequence of operations may be broken by go to statements, which define their successor explicitly, and shortened by conditional statements, which may cause certain statements to be skipped.

In order to make it possible to define a specific dynamic succession, statements may be provided with labels.

Since sequences of statements may be grouped together into compound statements and blocks the definition of statement must necessarily be recursive. Also since declarations, described in Section 5, enter fundamentally into the syntactic structure, the syntactic definition of statements must suppose declarations to be already defined.

4.1. COMPOUND STATEMENTS AND BLOCKS

4.1.1. SYNTAX

⟨unlabelled basic statement⟩ ::= ⟨assignment statement⟩ | ⟨go to statement⟩ |
   ⟨dummy statement⟩ | ⟨procedure statement⟩
⟨basic statement⟩ ::= ⟨unlabelled basic statement⟩ |
   ⟨label⟩:⟨basic statement⟩
⟨unconditional statement⟩ ::= ⟨basic statement⟩ |
   ⟨compound statement⟩ | ⟨block⟩
⟨statement⟩ ::= ⟨unconditional statement⟩ | ⟨conditional statement⟩ |
   ⟨for statement⟩
⟨compound tail⟩ ::= ⟨statement⟩ **end** | ⟨statement⟩;⟨compound tail⟩
⟨block head⟩ ::= **begin** ⟨declaration⟩ | ⟨block head⟩;⟨declaration⟩
⟨unlabelled compound⟩ ::= **begin** ⟨compound tail⟩
⟨unlabelled block⟩ ::= ⟨block head⟩;⟨compound tail⟩
⟨compound statement⟩ ::= ⟨unlabelled compound⟩ |
   ⟨label⟩:⟨compound statement⟩
⟨block⟩ ::= ⟨unlabelled block⟩ | ⟨label⟩:⟨block⟩
⟨program⟩ ::= ⟨block⟩ | ⟨compound statement⟩

This syntax may be illustrated as follows: Denoting arbitrary statements, declarations, and labels, by the letters S, D, and L, respectively, the basic syntactic units take the forms:

Compound statement:

L: L:... **begin** S; S;... S; S **end**

Block:

L: L:... **begin** D; D;... D; S; S;... S; S **end**

It should be kept in mind that each of the statements S may again be a complete compound statement or block.

4.1.2. EXAMPLES

Basic statements:

$a := p + q$
go to *Naples*
Start: *Continue*: $W := 7.993$

Compound statement:

begin $x := 0$; **for** $y := 1$ **step** 1 **until** n **do** $x := x + A[y]$;
    if $x > q$ **then go to** *STOP* **else if** $x > w - 2$ **then go to** S;
    Aw: St: $W := x + bob$ **end**

Block:

Q: **begin integer** i, k; **real** w;
        for $i := 1$ **step** 1 **until** m **do**
            for $k := i + 1$ **step** 1 **until** m **do**
            begin $w := A[i, k]$;
                $A[i, k] := A[k, i]$;
                $A[k, i] := w$
            end *for i and k*
        end *block Q*

4.1.3. SEMANTICS

Every block automatically introduces a new level of nomenclature. This is realized as follows: Any identifier occurring within the block may through a suitable declaration (cf. Section 5. Declarations) be specified to be local to the block in question. This means (a) that the entity represented by this identifier inside the block has no existence outside it and (b) that any entity represented by this identifier outside the block is completely inaccessible inside the block.

Identifiers (except those representing labels) occurring within a block and not being declared to this block will be nonlocal to it, i.e., will represent the same entity inside the block and in the level immediately outside it. A label separated by a colon from a statement, i.e., labelling that statement, behaves as though declared in the head of the smallest embracing block, i.e., the smallest block whose brackets **begin** and **end** enclose that statement. In this context a procedure body must be considered as if it were enclosed by **begin** and **end** and treated as a block.

Since a statement of a block may again itself be a block the concepts local and nonlocal to a block must be understood recursively. Thus an identifier, which is nonlocal to a block A, may or may not be nonlocal to the block B in which A is one statement.

4.2. ASSIGNMENT STATEMENTS

4.2.1. SYNTAX

⟨left part⟩ ::= ⟨variable⟩ := | ⟨procedure identifier⟩ :=
⟨left part list⟩ ::= ⟨left part⟩ | ⟨left part list⟩⟨left part⟩
⟨assignment statement⟩ ::= ⟨left part list⟩⟨arithmetic expression⟩ |
  ⟨left part list⟩⟨Boolean expression⟩

4.2.2. EXAMPLES

$$s := p[0] := n := n + 1 + s$$
$$n := n + 1$$
$$A := B/C - v - q \times S$$
$$S[v, k + 2] := 3 - arctan (s \times zeta)$$
$$V := Q > Y \wedge Z$$

4.2.3. SEMANTICS

Assignment statements serve for assigning the value of an expression to one or several variables or procedure identifiers. Assignment to a procedure identifier may only occur within the body of a procedure defining the value of a function designator (cf. Section 5.4.4). The process will in the general case be understood to take place in three steps as follows:

4.2.3.1. Any subscript expressions occurring in the left part variables are evaluated in sequence from left to right.

4.2.3.2. The expression of the statement is evaluated.

4.2.3.3. The value of the expression is assigned to all the left part variables, with any subscript expressions having values as evaluated in Step *4.2.3.1.*

4.2.4. TYPES

The type associated with all variables and procedure identifiers of a left part list must be the same. If this type is **Boolean**, the expression must likewise be **Boolean**. If the type is **real** or **integer**, the expression must be arithmetic. If the type of the arithmetic expression differs from that associated with the variables and procedure identifiers, appropriate transfer functions are understood to be automatically invoked. For transfer from **real** to **integer** type the transfer function is understood to yield a result equivalent to

$$entier (E + 0.5)$$

where E is the value of the expression. The type associated with a procedure identifier is given by the declarator which appears as the first symbol of the corresponding procedure declaration (cf. Section 5.4.4).

4.3. GO TO STATEMENTS

4.3.1. SYNTAX

⟨go to statement⟩ ::= **go to** ⟨designational expression⟩

4.3.2. EXAMPLES

> **go to** *8*
> **go to** *exit* [*n* + *1*]
> **go to** *Town* [**if** *y* < *0* **then** *N* **else** *N* + *1*]
> **go to if** *Ab* < *c* **then** *17* **else** *q* [**if** *w* < *0* **then** *2* **else** *n*]

4.3.3. SEMANTICS

A go to statement interrupts the normal sequence of operations, defined by the write-up of statements, by defining its successor explicitly by the value of a designational expression. Thus the next statement to be executed will be the one having this value as its label.

4.3.4. RESTRICTION

Since labels are inherently local, no go to statement can lead from outside into a block. A go to statement may, however, lead from outside into a compound statement.

4.3.5. GO TO AN UNDEFINED SWITCH DESIGNATOR

A go to statement is equivalent to a dummy statement if the designational expression is a switch designator whose value is undefined.

4.4. DUMMY STATEMENTS

4.4.1. SYNTAX

⟨dummy statement⟩ ::= ⟨empty⟩

4.4.2. EXAMPLES

L:

begin ... ; *John*: **end**

4.4.3. SEMANTICS

A dummy statement executes no operation. It may serve to place a label.

4.5. CONDITIONAL STATEMENTS

4.5.1. SYNTAX

⟨if clause⟩ ::= **if** ⟨Boolean expression⟩ **then**
⟨unconditional statement⟩ ::= ⟨basic statement⟩ | ⟨compound statement⟩ |
    ⟨block⟩
⟨if statement⟩ ::= ⟨if clause⟩⟨unconditional statement⟩
⟨conditional statement⟩ ::= ⟨if statement⟩ | ⟨if statement⟩ **else** ⟨statement⟩ |
    ⟨if clause⟩⟨for statement⟩ | ⟨label⟩:⟨conditional statement⟩

4.5.2. EXAMPLES

if $x > 0$ **then** $n := n + 1$

if $v > u$ **then** $V: q := n + m$ **else go to** R

if $s < 0 \lor P \leqq Q$ **then** $AA:$ **begin if** $q < v$ **then** $a := v/s$

                        else $y := 2 \times a$ **end else if** $v > s$ **then** $a := v - q$

                        else if $v > s - 1$ **then go to** S

4.5.3. SEMANTICS

Conditional statements cause certain statements to be executed or skipped depending on the running values of specified Boolean expressions.

4.5.3.1. If statement. The unconditional statement of an if statement will be executed if the Boolean expression of the if clause is true. Otherwise it will be skipped and the operation will be continued with the next statement.

4.5.3.2. Conditional statement. According to the syntax two different forms of conditional statements are possible. These may be illustrated as follows:

if B1 **then** S1 **else if** B2 **then** S2 **else** S3; S4

and

if B1 **then** S1 **else if** B2 **then** S2 **else if** B3 **then** S3; S4

Here B1 to B3 are Boolean expressions, while S1 to S3 are unconditional statements. S4 is the statement following the complete conditional statement.

The execution of a conditional statement may be described as follows: The Boolean expressions of the if clauses are evaluated one after the other in sequence from left to right until one yielding the value **true** is found. Then the unconditional statement following this Boolean is executed. Unless this statement defines its successor explicitly the next statement to be executed will be S4, i.e., the statement following the complete conditional statement. Thus the effect of the delimiter **else** may be described by saying that it defines the successor of the statement it follows to be the statement following the complete conditional statement.

The construction

else ⟨unconditional statement⟩

is equivalent to

else if true then ⟨unconditional statement⟩

If none of the Boolean expressions of the if clauses is true, the effect of the whole conditional statement will be equivalent to that of a dummy statement.

For further explanation the following picture may be useful:

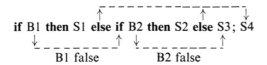

if B1 **then** S1 **else if** B2 **then** S2 **else** S3; S4

        B1 false   B2 false

4.5.4. GO TO INTO A CONDITIONAL STATEMENT

The effect of a go to statement leading into a conditional statement follows directly from the above explanation of the effect of **else**.

4.6. FOR STATEMENTS

4.6.1. SYNTAX

⟨for list element⟩ ::= ⟨arithmetic expression⟩ |
  ⟨arithmetic expression⟩ **step** ⟨arithmetic expression⟩ **until**
  ⟨arithmetic expression⟩ |
  ⟨arithmetic expression⟩ **while** ⟨Boolean expression⟩
⟨for list⟩ ::= ⟨for list element⟩ | ⟨for list⟩, ⟨for list element⟩
⟨for clause⟩ ::= **for** ⟨variable⟩ := ⟨for list⟩ **do**
⟨for statement⟩ ::= ⟨for clause⟩⟨statement⟩ | ⟨label⟩:⟨for statement⟩

4.6.2. EXAMPLES

      for $q := 1$ **step** s **until** n **do** $A[q] := B[q]$
      for $k := 1, V1 \times 2$ **while** $V1 < N$ **do**
      for $j := I + G, L, 1$ **step** 1 **until** $N, C + D$ **do** $A[k,j] := B[k,j]$

4.6.3. SEMANTICS

A for clause causes the statement S which it precedes to be repeatedly executed zero or more times. In addition it performs a sequence of assignments to its controlled variable. The process may be visualized by means of the following picture:

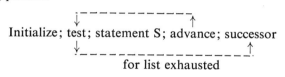

Initialize; test; statement S; advance; successor

for list exhausted

In this picture the word initialize means: perform the first assignment of the for clause. Advance means: perform the next assignment of the for clause. Test determines if the last assignment has been done. If so, the execution continues with the successor of the for statement. If not, the statement following the for clause is executed.

4.6.4. THE FOR LIST ELEMENTS

The for list gives a rule for obtaining the values which are consecutively assigned to the controlled variable. This sequence of values is obtained from the for list elements by taking these one by one in the order in which they are written. The sequence of values generated by each of the three species of for list elements and the corresponding execution of the statement S are given by the following rules:

4.6.4.1. Arithmetic expression. This element gives rise to one value, namely the value of the given arithmetic expression as calculated immediately before the corresponding execution of the statement S.

4.6.4.2. Step-until-element. An element of the form A **step** B **until** C, where A, B, and C are arithmetic expressions, gives rise to an execution which may be described most concisely in terms of additional ALGOL statements as follows:

V := A;
L1: **if** (V − C) × *sign* (B) > *0* **then go to** *Element exhausted*;
  Statement S;
  V := V + B;
  go to *L1*;

where V is the controlled variable of the for clause and *Element exhausted* points to the evaluation according to the next element in the for list, or if the step-until-element is the last of the list, to the next statement in the program.

4.6.4.3. While-element. The execution governed by a for list element of the form E **while** F, where E is an arithmetic and F a Boolean expression, is most concisely described in terms of additional ALGOL statements as follows:

L3: V := E;
  if ¬ F **then go to** *Element exhausted*;
  Statement S;
  go to *L3*;

where the notation is the same as in *4.6.4.2* above.

4.6.5. THE VALUE OF THE CONTROLLED VARIABLE UPON EXIT
  Upon exit out of the statement S (supposed to be compound) through a go to statement the value of the controlled variable will be the same as it was immediately preceding the execution of the go to statement.
  If the exit is due to exhaustion of the for list, on the other hand, the value of the controlled variable is undefined after the exit.

4.6.6. GO TO LEADING INTO A FOR STATEMENT
  The effect of a go to statement, outside a for statement, which refers to a label within the for statement, is undefined.

4.7. PROCEDURE STATEMENTS

4.7.1. SYNTAX
⟨actual parameter⟩ ::= ⟨string⟩ | ⟨expression⟩ | ⟨array identifier⟩ |
  ⟨switch identifier⟩ | ⟨procedure identifier⟩
⟨letter string⟩ ::= ⟨letter⟩ | ⟨letter string⟩⟨letter⟩
⟨parameter delimiter⟩ ::= , |) ⟨letter string⟩:(
⟨actual parameter list⟩ ::= ⟨actual parameter⟩ |
  ⟨actual parameter list⟩⟨parameter delimiter⟩⟨actual parameter⟩
⟨actual parameter part⟩ ::= ⟨empty⟩ | (⟨actual parameter list⟩)
⟨procedure statement⟩ ::= ⟨procedure identifier⟩⟨actual parameter part⟩

4.7.2. EXAMPLES

Spur (*A*) Order: (*7*) Result to: (*V*)
Transpose (*W*, *v* + *I*)
Absmax (*A*, *N*, *M*, *Yy*, *I*, *K*)
Innerproduct (*A*[*t*, *P*, *u*], *B*[*P*], *10*, *P*, *Y*)

These examples correspond to examples given in Section 5.4.2.

4.7.3. SEMANTICS

A procedure statement serves to invoke (call for) the execution of a procedure body (cf. Section 5.4. Procedure declarations). Where the procedure body is a statement written in ALGOL the effect of this execution will be equivalent to the effect of performing the following operations on the program at the time of execution of the procedure statement:

4.7.3.1. Value assignment (call by value). All formal parameters quoted in the value part of the procedure declaration heading are assigned the values (cf. Section 2.8. Values and types) of the corresponding actual parameters, these assignments being considered as being performed explicitly before entering the procedure body. The effect is as though an additional block embracing the procedure body were created in which these assignments were made to variables local to this fictitious block with types as given in the corresponding specifications (cf. Section 5.4.5). As a consequence, variables called by value are to be considered as nonlocal to the body of the procedure, but local to the fictitious block (cf. Section 5.4.3).

4.7.3.2. Name replacement (call by name). Any formal parameter not quoted in the value list is replaced, throughout the procedure body, by the corresponding actual parameter, after enclosing this latter in parentheses wherever syntactically possible. Possible conflicts between identifiers inserted through this process and other identifiers already present within the procedure body will be avoided by suitable systematic changes of the formal or local identifiers involved.

4.7.3.3. Body replacement and execution. Finally the procedure body, modified as above, is inserted in place of the procedure statement and executed. If the procedure is called from a place outside the scope of any nonlocal quantity of the procedure body the conflicts between the identifiers inserted through this process of body replacement and the identifiers whose declarations are valid at the place of the procedure statement or function designator will be avoided through suitable systematic changes of the latter identifiers.

4.7.4. ACTUAL-FORMAL CORRESPONDENCE

The correspondence between the actual parameters of the procedure statement and the formal parameters of the procedure heading is established as follows: The actual parameter list of the procedure statement must have the same number of entries as the formal parameter list of the procedure declaration heading. The correspondence is obtained by taking the entries of these two lists in the same order.

4.7.5. RESTRICTIONS

For a procedure statement to be defined it is evidently necessary that the operations on the procedure body defined in Sections *4.7.3.1* and *4.7.3.2* lead to a correct ALGOL statement.

This imposes the restriction on any procedure statement that the kind and type of each actual parameter be compatible with the kind and type of the corresponding formal parameter. Some important particular cases of this general rule are the following:

4.7.5.1. If a string is supplied as an actual parameter in a procedure statement or function designator, whose defining procedure body is an ALGOL 60 statement (as opposed to non-ALGOL code, cf. Section 4.7.8), then this string can only be used within the procedure body as an actual parameter in further procedure calls. Ultimately it can only be used by a procedure body expressed in non-ALGOL code.

4.7.5.2. A formal parameter which occurs as a left part variable in an assignment statement within the procedure body and which is not called by value can only correspond to an actual parameter which is a variable (special case of expression).

4.7.5.3. A formal parameter which is used within the procedure body as an array identifier can only correspond to an actual parameter which is an array identifier of an array of the same dimensions. In addition if the formal parameter is called by value the local array created during the call will have the same subscript bounds as the actual array.

4.7.5.4. A formal parameter which is called by value cannot in general correspond to a switch identifier or a procedure identifier or a string, because these latter do not possess values (the exception is the procedure identifier of a procedure declaration which has an empty formal parameter part (cf. Section 5.4.1) and which defines the value of a function designator (cf. Section 5.4.4). This procedure identifier is in itself a complete expression).

4.7.5.5. Any formal parameter may have restrictions on the type of the corresponding actual parameter associated with it (these restrictions may, or may not, be given through specifications in the procedure heading). In the procedure statement such restrictions must evidently be observed.

4.7.6. DELETED

4.7.7. PARAMETER DELIMITERS

All parameter delimiters are understood to be equivalent. No correspondence between the parameter delimiters used in a procedure statement and those used in the procedure heading is expected beyond their number being the same. Thus the information conveyed by using the elaborate ones is entirely optional.

4.7.8. PROCEDURE BODY EXPRESSED IN CODE

The restrictions imposed on a procedure statement calling a procedure having its body expressed in non-ALGOL code evidently can only be derived from the characteristics of the code used and the intent of the user and thus fall outside the scope of the reference language.

5. DECLARATIONS

Declarations serve to define certain properties of the quantities used in the program, and to associate them with identifiers. A declaration of an identifier is valid for one block. Outside this block the particular identifier may be used for other purposes (cf. Section 4.1.3).

Dynamically this implies the following: at the time of an entry into a block (through the **begin** since the labels inside are local and therefore inaccessible from outside) all identifiers declared for the block assume the significance implied by the nature of the declarations given. If these identifiers had already been defined by other declarations outside they are for the time being given a new significance. Identifiers which are not declared for the block, on the other hand, retain their old meaning.

At the time of an exit from a block (through **end**, or by a go to statement) all identifiers which are declared for the block lose their local significance.

A declaration may be marked with the additional declarator **own**. This has the following effect: upon a reentry into the block, the values of own quantities will be unchanged from their values at the last exit, while the values of declared variables which are not marked as own are undefined. Apart from labels and formal parameters of procedure declarations and with the possible exception of those for standard functions (cf. Sections 3.2.4 and 3.2.5) all identifiers of a program must be declared. No identifier may be declared more than once in any one block head.

Syntax.

⟨declaration⟩ ::= ⟨type declaration⟩ | ⟨array declaration⟩ |
⟨switch declaration⟩ | ⟨procedure declaration⟩

5.1. TYPE DECLARATIONS

5.1.1. SYNTAX

⟨type list⟩ ::= ⟨simple variable⟩ | ⟨simple variable⟩, ⟨type list⟩
⟨type⟩ ::= **real** | **integer** | **Boolean**
⟨local or own type⟩ ::= ⟨type⟩ | **own** ⟨type⟩
⟨type declaration⟩ ::= ⟨local or own type⟩⟨type list⟩

5.1.2. EXAMPLES

integer p, q, s

own Boolean *Acryl*, *n*

5.1.3. SEMANTICS

Type declarations serve to declare certain identifiers to represent simple variables of a given type. Real declared variables may only assume positive or negative values including zero. Integer declared variables may only assume positive and negative integral values including zero. Boolean declared variables may only assume the values **true** and **false**.

In arithmetic expressions any position which can be occupied by a real declared variable may be occupied by an integer declared variable.

For the semantics of **own**, see the fourth paragraph of Section 5 above.

5.2. ARRAY DECLARATIONS

5.2.1. SYNTAX

⟨lower bound⟩ ::= ⟨arithmetic expression⟩
⟨upper bound⟩ ::= ⟨arithmetic expression⟩
⟨bound pair⟩ ::= ⟨lower bound⟩:⟨upper bound⟩
⟨bound pair list⟩ ::= ⟨bound pair⟩ | ⟨bound pair list⟩, ⟨bound pair⟩
⟨array segment⟩ ::= ⟨array identifier⟩[⟨bound pair list⟩] |
    ⟨array identifier⟩, ⟨array segment⟩
⟨array list⟩ ::= ⟨array segment⟩ | ⟨array list⟩, ⟨array segment⟩
⟨array declaration⟩ ::= **array** ⟨array list⟩ |
    ⟨local or own type⟩ **array** ⟨array list⟩

5.2.2. EXAMPLES

array a, b, $c[7 : n, 2 : m]$, $s[-2 : 10]$

own integer array A [**if** $c < 0$ **then** 2 **else** $1 : 20$]

real array $q[-7 : -1]$

5.2.3. SEMANTICS

An array declaration declares one or several identifiers to represent multi-dimensional arrays of subscripted variables and gives the dimensions of the arrays, the bounds of the subscripts, and the types of the variables.

5.2.3.1. Subscript bounds. The subscript bounds for any array are given in the first subscript bracket following the identifier of this array in the form of a bound pair list. Each item of this list gives the lower and upper bound of a subscript in the form of two arithmetic expressions separated by the delimiter : . The bound pair list gives the bounds of all subscripts taken in order from left to right.

5.2.3.2. Dimensions. The dimensions are given as the number of entries in the bound pair lists.

5.2.3.3. Types. All arrays declared in one declaration are of the same quoted type. If no type declarator is given the type **real** is understood.

5.2.4. LOWER UPPER BOUND EXPRESSIONS

5.2.4.1. The expressions will be evaluated in the same way as subscript expressions (cf. Section 3.1.4.2).

5.2.4.2. The expressions can only depend on variables and procedures which are nonlocal to the block for which the array declaration is valid. Consequently in the outermost block of a program only array declarations with constant bounds may be declared.

5.2.4.3. An array is defined only when the values of all upper subscript bounds are not smaller than those of the corresponding lower bounds.

5.2.4.4. The expressions will be evaluated once at each entrance into the block.

5.2.5. THE IDENTITY OF SUBSCRIPTED VARIABLES

The identity of a subscripted variable is not related to the subscript bounds given in the array declaration. However, even if an array is declared **own** the values of the corresponding subscripted variables will, at any time, be defined only for those of these variables which have subscripts within the most recently calculated subscript bounds.

5.3. SWITCH DECLARATIONS

5.3.1. SYNTAX

⟨switch list⟩ ::= ⟨designational expression⟩ |
    ⟨switch list⟩, ⟨designational expression⟩
⟨switch declaration⟩ ::= **switch** ⟨switch identifier⟩ := ⟨switch list⟩

5.3.2. EXAMPLES

        switch S := $S1$, $S2$, $Q[m]$, **if** $v > -5$ **then** $S3$ **else** $S4$
        switch Q := $P1$, w

5.3.3. SEMANTICS

A switch declaration defines the set of values of the corresponding switch designators. These values are given one by one as the values of the designational expressions entered in the switch list. With each of these designational expressions there is associated a positive integer, $1, 2, \ldots$, obtained by counting the items in the list from left to right. The value of the switch designator corresponding to a given value of the subscript expression (cf. Section 3.5. Designational expressions) is the value of the designational expression in the switch list having this given value as its associated integer.

5.3.4. EVALUATION OF EXPRESSIONS IN THE SWITCH LIST

An expression in the switch list will be evaluated every time the item of the list in which the expression occurs is referred to, using the current values of all variables involved.

5.3.5. INFLUENCE OF SCOPES

If a switch designator occurs outside the scope of a quantity entering into a designational expression in the switch list, and an evaluation of this switch designator selects this designational expression, then the conflicts between the identifiers for the quantities in this expression and the identifiers whose declarations are valid at the place of the switch designator will be avoided through suitable systematic changes of the latter identifiers.

5.4. PROCEDURE DECLARATIONS

5.4.1. SYNTAX

⟨formal parameter⟩ ::= ⟨identifier⟩
⟨formal parameter list⟩ ::= ⟨formal parameter⟩ |
    ⟨formal parameter list⟩⟨parameter delimiter⟩⟨formal parameter⟩
⟨formal parameter part⟩ ::= ⟨empty⟩ | (⟨formal parameter list⟩)
⟨identifier list⟩ ::= ⟨identifier⟩ | ⟨identifier list⟩, ⟨identifier⟩
⟨value part⟩ ::= **value** ⟨identifier list⟩; | ⟨empty⟩
⟨specifier⟩ ::= **string** | ⟨type⟩ | **array** | ⟨type⟩ **array** | **label** | **switch** |
    procedure | ⟨type⟩ **procedure**
⟨specification part⟩ ::= ⟨empty⟩ | ⟨specifier⟩⟨identifier list⟩; |
    ⟨specification part⟩⟨specifier⟩⟨identifier list⟩;
⟨procedure heading⟩ ::= ⟨procedure identifier⟩⟨formal parameter part⟩;
    ⟨value part⟩⟨specification part⟩
⟨procedure body⟩ ::= ⟨statement⟩ | ⟨code⟩
⟨procedure declaration⟩ ::=
    procedure ⟨procedure heading⟩ ⟨procedure body⟩ |
    ⟨type⟩ **procedure** ⟨procedure heading⟩ ⟨procedure body⟩

5.4.2. EXAMPLES (see also the examples at the end of the report).
procedure *Spur* (*a*) Order: (*n*) Result: (*s*); **value** *n*;
array *a*; **integer** *n*; **real** *s*;
    begin integer *k*;
    $s := 0$;
    for $k := 1$ **step** 1 **until** n **do** $s := s + a[k, k]$
    end

procedure *Transpose* (*a*) Order: (*n*); **value** *n*;
array *a*; **integer** *n*;
    begin real *w*; **integer** *i*, *k*;
    for $i := 1$ **step** 1 **until** n **do**
        for $k := 1 + i$ **step** 1 **until** n **do**
            begin $w := a[i, k]$;
            $a[i, k] := a[k, i]$;
            $a[k, i] := w$
            end
    end *Transpose*

integer procedure *Step* (*u*); **real** *u*;
Step := **if** $0 \leq u \wedge u \leq 1$ **then** *1* **else** *0*

procedure *Absmax* (*a*) size: (*n*, *m*) Result: (*y*) Subscripts: (*i*, *k*);
comment The absolute greatest element of the matrix *a*, of size *n* by *m* is
transferred to *y*, and the subscripts of this element to *i* and *k*;
array *a*; **integer** *n*, *m*, *i*, *k*; **real** *y*;
  begin integer *p*, *q*;
    y := *0*;
    for *p* := *1* **step** *1* **until** *n* **do for** *q* := *1* **step** *1* **until** *m* **do**
    if *abs* (*a*[*p*, *q*]) > *y* **then begin** *y* := *abs*(*a*[*p*, *q*]); *i* := *p*; *k* := *q* **end**
  end *Absmax*

procedure *Innerproduct* (*a*, *b*) Order: (*k*, *p*) Result: (*y*); **value** *k*;
integer *k*, *p*; **real** *y*, *a*, *b*;
  begin real *s*;
    s := *0*;
    for *p* := *1* **step** *1* **until** *k* **do** *s* := *s* + *a* × *b*;
    y := *s*
  end *Innerproduct*

5.4.3. SEMANTICS

A procedure declaration serves to define the procedure associated with a
procedure identifier. The principal constituent of a procedure declaration is
a statement or a piece of code, the procedure body, which through the use of
procedure statements and/or function designators may be activated from
other parts of the block in the head of which the procedure declaration
appears. Associated with the body is a heading, which specifies certain
identifiers occurring within the body to represent formal parameters. Formal
parameters in the procedure body will, whenever the procedure is activated
(cf. Section 3.2. Function designators and Section 4.7. Procedure statements)
be assigned the values of or replaced by actual parameters. Identifiers in the
procedure body which are not formal will be either local or nonlocal to the
body depending on whether they are declared within the body or not. Those
of them which are nonlocal to the body may well be local to the block in the
head of which the procedure declaration appears. The procedure body always
acts like a block, whether it has the form of one or not. Consequently the
scope of any label labelling a statement within the body or the body itself can
never extend beyond the procedure body. In addition, if the identifier of a
formal parameter is declared anew within the procedure body (including the
case of its use as a label as in Section 4.1.3), it is thereby given a local
significance and actual parameters which correspond to it are inaccessible
throughout the scope of this inner local quantity.

5.4.4. VALUES OF FUNCTION DESIGNATORS

For a procedure declaration to define the value of a function designator there must, within the procedure body, occur one or more explicit assignment statements with the procedure identifier in a left part; at least one of these must be executed, and the type associated with the procedure identifier must be declared through the appearance of a type declarator as the very first symbol of the procedure declaration. The last value so assigned is used to continue the evaluation of the expression in which the function designator occurs. Any occurrence of the procedure identifier within the body of the procedure other than in a left part in an assignment statement denotes activation of the procedure.

5.4.5. SPECIFICATIONS

In the heading a specification part, giving information about the kinds and types of the formal parameters by means of an abvious notation, may be included. In this part no formal parameter may occur more than once. Specifications of formal parameters called by value (cf. Section *4.7.3.1*) must be supplied and specifications of formal parameters called by name (cf. Section *4.7.3.2*) may be omitted.

5.4.6. CODE AS PROCEDURE BODY

It is understood that the procedure body may be expressed in non-ALGOL language. Since it is intended that the use of this feature should be entirely a question of hardware representation, no further rules concerning this code language can be given within the reference language.

EXAMPLES OF PROCEDURE DECLARATIONS

EXAMPLE 1

procedure *euler* (*fct, sum, eps, tim*); **value** *eps, tim*; **integer** *tim*;
real procedure *fct*; **real** *sum, eps*;
comment *euler* computes the sum of *fct(i)* for *i* from zero up to infinity by means of a suitably refined euler transformation. The summation is stopped as soon as *tim* times in succession the absolute value of the terms of the transformed series are found to be less than *eps*. Hence, one should provide a function *fct* with one integer argument, an upper bound *eps*, and an integer *tim*. The output is the sum *sum*. *euler* is particularly efficient in the case of a slowly convergent or divergent alternating series;
    begin integer *i, k, n, t*; **array** $m[0:15]$; **real** *mn, mp, ds*;
    $i := n := t := 0$; $m[0] := fct(0)$; $sum := m[0]/2$;
next term:
      $i := i + 1$; $mn := fct(i)$;
      for $k := 0$ **step** *1* **until** *n* **do**
        begin $mp := (mn + m[k])/2$; $m[k] := mn$; $mn := mp$ **end** *means*;
      if $(abs(mn) < abs(m[n])) \wedge (n < 15)$ **then**
        begin $ds := mn/2$; $n := n + 1$; $m[n] := mn$ **end** *accept*

else *ds* := *mn*;
sum := *sum* + *ds*;
if *abs*(*ds*) < *eps* then *t* := *t* + *1* else *t* := *0*;
if *t* < *tim* then **go to** *next term*
end *euler*

EXAMPLE 2[1]

procedure *RK*(*x*, *y*, *n*, *FKT*, *eps*, *eta*, *xE*, *yE*, *fi*); **value** *x*, *y*; **integer** *n*;
Boolean *fi*; **real** *x*, *eps*, *eta*, *xE*; **array** *y*, *yE*; **procedure** *FKT*;
comment *RK* integrates the system $y'_k = f_k(x, y_1, y_2, \ldots, y_n)$ ($k = 1, 2, \ldots n$)
of differential equations with the method of Runge-Kutta with automatic
search for appropriate length of integration step. Parameters are: The
initial values *x* and *y*[*k*] for *x* and the unknown functions $y_k(x)$. The order *n*
of the system. The procedure *FKT*(*x*, *y*, *n*, *z*) which represents the system to
be integrated, i.e., the set of functions f_k. The tolerance values *eps* and *eta*
which govern the accuracy of the numerical integration. The end of the
integration interval *xE*. The output parameter *yE* which represents the
solution at *x* = *xE*. The Boolean variable *fi*, which must always be given the
value **true** for an isolated or first entry into *RK*. If however the functions *y*
must be available at several meshpoints $x_0, x_1, \ldots, x_n$, then the procedure
must be called repeatedly (with $x = x_k$, $xE = x_{k+1}$, for $k = 0, 1, \ldots, n - 1$)
and then the later calls may occur with *fi* = **false** which saves computing
time. The input parameters of *FKT* must be *x*, *y*, *n*, the output parameter *z*
represents the set of derivatives $z[k] = f_k(x, y[1], y[2], \ldots, y[n])$ for *x* and
the actual *y*'s. A procedure *comp* enters as a nonlocal identifier;

begin
    array *z*, *y1*, *y2*, *y3*[*1* : *n*]; **real** *x1*, *x2*, *x3*, *H*; **Boolean** *out*;
    integer *k*, *j*; **own real** *s*, *Hs*;
    procedure *RK1ST*(*x*, *y*, *h*, *xe*, *ye*); **real** *x*, *h*, *xe*; **array** *y*, *ye*;
        comment *RK1ST* integrates one single Runge-Kutta step with initial
        values *x*, *y*[*k*] which yields the output parameters *xe* = *x* + *h* and
        ye[*k*], the latter being the solution at *xe*.
        Important: the parameters *n*, *FKT*, *z* enter *RK1ST* as nonlocal
        entities;

---

[1] This RK-program contains some new ideas which are related to ideas of S. GILL,
A process for the step by step integration of differential equations in an automatic
computing machine. *Proc. Camb. Phil. Soc.* **47** (1951) p. 96, and E. FRÖBERG, On the
solution of ordinary differential equations with digital computing machines, *Fysiograf.
Sällsk. Lund, Förhd.* **20** Nr. 11 (1950) pp. 136–152. It must be clear, however, that with
respect to computing time and round-off errors it may not be optimal, nor has it actually
been tested on a computer.

```
begin
    array w[1 : n], a[1 : 5]; integer k, j;
    a[1] := a[2] := a[5] := h/2; a[3] := a[4] := h; xe := x;
    for k := 1 step 1 until n do ye[k] := w[k] := y[k];
    for j := 1 step 1 until 4 do
        begin
            FKT(xe, w, n, z);
            xe := x + a[j];
            for k := 1 step 1 until n do
                begin
                    w[k] := y[k] + a[j] × z[k];
                    ye[k] := ye[k] + a[j + 1] × z[k]/3
                end k
        end j
    end RK1ST;
```

Begin of program:
```
    if fi then begin H := xE − x; s := 0 end else H := Hs;
    out := false;
AA: if (x + 2.01 × H − xE > 0) ≡ (H > 0) then
    begin Hs := H; out := true; H := (xE − x)/2 end if;
    RK1ST(x, y, 2 × H, x1, y1);
BB: RK1ST(x, y, H, x2, y2); RK1ST(x2, y2, H, x3, y3);
    for k := 1 step 1 until n do
        if comp(y1[k], y3[k], eta) > eps then go to CC;
    comment comp(a, b, c) is a function designator, the value of which is the
    absolute value of the difference of the mantissae of a and b, after the
    exponents of these quantities have been made equal to the largest of
    the exponents of the originally given parameters a, b, c;
    x := x3; if out then go to DD;
    for k := 1 step 1 until n do y[k] := y3[k];
    if s = 5 then begin s := 0; H := 2 × H end if;
    s := s + 1; go to AA;
CC: H := 0.5 × H; out := false; x1 := x2;
    for k := 1 step 1 until n do y1[k] := y2[k];
    go to BB;
DD: for k := 1 step 1 until n do yE[k] := y3[k]
end RK
```

ALPHABETIC INDEX OF DEFINITIONS
OF CONCEPTS AND SYNTACTIC UNITS

All references are given through section numbers. The references are given in three groups:

<dl>

def   Following the abbreviation "def", reference to the syntactic definition (if any) is given.

synt   Following the abbreviation "synt", references to the occurrences in metalinguistic formulae are given. References already quoted in the def-group are not repeated.

text   Following the word "text", the references to definitions given in the text are given.

</dl>

The basic symbols represented by signs other than underlined words have been collected at the beginning. The examples have been ignored in compiling the index.

$+$, *see* plus

$-$, *see* minus

$\times$, *see* multiply

$/$, $\div$, *see* divide

$\uparrow$, *see* exponentiation

$<$, $\leqq$, $=$, $\geqq$, $>$, $\neq$, *see* ⟨relational operator⟩

$\equiv$, $\supset$, $\vee$, $\wedge$, $\neg$, *see* ⟨logical operator⟩

, , *see* comma

. , *see* decimal point

$_{10}$, *see* ten

: , *see* colon

; , *see* semicolon

$:=$, *see* colon equal

⊔, *see* space

( ), *see* parentheses

[ ], *see* subscript bracket

' ', *see* string quote

⟨actual parameter⟩, def 3.2.1, 4.7.1

⟨actual parameter list⟩, def 3.2.1, 4.7.1

⟨actual parameter part⟩, def 3.2.1, 4.7.1

⟨adding operator⟩, def 3.3.1

alphabet, text 2.1

arithmetic, text 3.3.6

⟨arithmetic expression⟩, def 3.3.1 synt 3, 3.1.1, 3.3.1, 3.4.1, 4.2.1, 4.6.1, 5.2.1 text 3.3.3

⟨arithmetic operator⟩, def 2.3 text 3.3.4

array, synt 2.3, 5.2.1, 5.4.1

array, text 3.1.4.1

⟨array declaration⟩, def 5.2.1 synt 5 text 5.2.3

⟨array identifier⟩, def 3.1.1 synt 3.2.1, 4.7.1, 5.2.1 text 2.8

⟨array list⟩, def 5.2.1

⟨array segment⟩, def 5.2.1

⟨assignment statement⟩, def 4.2.1 synt 4.1.1 text 1, 4.2.3

133

SUBJECT INDEX

Abbreviation of number representation, (1.2.)
abs, (2.4.)
Actual:
  expression, (10.1.1.)
  expressions as arguments, (11.1.)
  expressions as results, (10.1.2.2, 11.2.)
  parameter, (10.1.1.)
  parameter list, (10.2.)
  quantity, (10.1.1.)
  rules concerning them at procedure call, (10.2.)
Addition, (2.1., 8.1.)
Alternative, **if** . . . **then** . . . **else** . . . , (5.3.).
    See also Conditional statement, Conditional expression
And, (8., 8.1.)
arctan, (2.4.)
Arguments, (10.1.2., 10.1.2.1.)
  expressions as . . . , (11.1.)
Arithmetic expression, (2.)
  conditional, (8.3.)
  construction, (2.3.)
  denominator of, (2.1.)
  evaluation, (2.3., 2.3.1., 8.1.)
  numerical, (2.1.)
Arithmetic operator, (2.1., 8.1.)
Array, **array,** (1.4.)
  actual, (10.2.)
  components of an, (4.2., 4.2.1.)
  corresponding components, (10.1.2.1.)
  declaration, (4.2., 4.2.1.)
  dynamic declaration, (7.4.)
  formal, (10.1.2.1.)
  identifier, (4.2.1.)

Array (*cont.*):
  identifier in a procedure, (10.1.1., 10.1.2.1.)
  type of an . . . , (4.2.1., 8.2.)
Asymmetrical form of the conditional statement, (5.2.)
Assignment, (2.3.)
  of a logical value, (8.2.)
  of numerical values through expressions, (2.3.)
  of numerical values through input, (2.2.2.)
Assignment statement, (2.2.2., 2.3.2.)
  brief description, (3.1.)
  form, (2.3.)
  left part, (2.3.2.)
  mixed types, (2.3.2., 8.2.)
  multiple, (2.3.4.)
Assignment symbol :=, (2.3., 2.3.3.)
  special meaning, (2.3.3.)
  used in loops, (4.1., 6.4.)
  used in switches, (9.2.)
Assignment to subscripted variables, (4.2,2.)
Assigned value, (7.3.)
Attached:
  label . . . to a statement, (6.1.)

Base, (2.1.)
Basic symbol, (1., 1.1.)
begin, (1.4.)
  used in:
    block, (7.1.)
    compound statement, (3.2.)
    program, (3.3.)

137